THE PROBLEM SOLVERS

A series of profiles of contemporary industrial scientists. The author has carefully prepared a portrait-in-the-making of the people who today are responsible for our progress in business and industry. While some names of the individuals may not be easily recognizable, their achievements and contributions are well known and in some cases vital to our well-being. An engineer today does not have to be tied to a drawing board. If he has the desire and know-how, he can look forward to a future of research and leadership and there is no limit to the heights he may reach.

The
Problem Solvers

by Adrian A. Paradis

G. P. Putnam's Sons　　New York

1255877

CONTENTS

OTHER PUTNAM BOOKS ABOUT PEOPLE AND EVENTS

THE GREAT DOCTORS
By Robert Silverberg

THE RUSSIAN REVOLUTIONS
By David Footman

TO THE READER

The period since World War II has truly been an age of science. It has been said that during the decade and a half between 1945 and 1961 additional scientific knowledge equaled all that scientists knew prior to 1945. Every day scientists make new discoveries, and this seems especially true in the case of space science. To read the papers one might think that all scientific endeavor is being concentrated on developing guided missiles, orbiting satellites and thrusting man into outer space.

These are worthy aims because they are essential to our defense and at the same time they widen our knowledge and understanding of the universe. Just as important to the betterment, happiness and comfort of mankind, however, are the other scientific programs conducted by business and industry. You will find engineers and scientists not only working on problems of defense and outer space but developing such things as life-saving medicines, more nutritious foods, new miracle fibers, better television receivers, safer automobiles, improved cameras, swifter helicopters, more comfortable homes and a host of other things.

In the United States more than $15,000,000,000 is spent annually on research and development, and this requires a technical staff of almost 1,500,000 men and women. Business and industry perform three-quarters of this work either for their own needs or for the government. Approximately 70 percent of the funds are spent on development, 10 percent on basic research and 20 percent on applied research.

Some of the research is so basic or abstract that a com-

7

pany cannot expect to profit from it for some time. In 1961, for example, at duPont $59,000,000 was spent on pioneering research studies, much of it for projects of no immediate commercial use. In the long range, however, such projects will probably result in profitable products and thus justify this expenditure of the stockholders' money.

Engineering offers an intriguing career to those who have an inquiring mind and a desire to contribute to the growing store of scientific knowledge. This book tells about engineers who, serving business and industry and through their research and ingenuity, have made notable contributions to our American way of life. Actually there are almost as many different kinds of engineers as there are industries, and today there are over 150 different engineering organizations, each devoted to a specialized interest.

As engineers become more specialized and at the same time widen their research efforts, it becomes increasingly difficult to draw a sharp distinction between engineers and scientists. It is generally agreed that the scientist is a man who makes discoveries whereas the engineer applies the discovery to a practical problem. Discussing this difference, Mr. Phil M. Ferguson wrote in the *Texas Professional Engineer*:

. . . While science has obviously expanded towards engineering, engineers have less conspicuously been moving towards specialized areas that would once have been considered pure science.

Inevitably we are rapidly approaching the time when the once sharp and clearly discernible dividing line between engineering and science becomes dim and lost in the overlapping of areas and functions. Is the metallurgist an engineer or a scientist? Some metallurgists are very fine engineers, some truly scientists, and a few equally engineer-scientists.

Telstar, the communications satellite, was the brainchild not of a scientist but an engineer, John R. Pierce. Many engineers claim that they have accomplished most of the developmental work on scientific triumphs. They say that engineers visualize and then discover how findings can be used to benefit society whereas scientists explore all the reasons why things happen. However, engineers and scientists are both invaluable to industry.

All of the men discussed in this book started their scientific careers in the research laboratory. As they became more proficient in their work some moved into positions where they explore the reasons why things happen, others were assigned to direct over-all company research effort, while several were groomed for top administrative positions.

The engineer is no longer a man who devotes his life to leaning over the drafting board, surveying land or working in the laboratory. Industry recognizes that the engineer is one of its most important employees and that he brings to the job a unique background and ability which qualifies him in many companies for key jobs—even that of chief executive officer.

Chapter 1

•

A MAN OF MANY PARTS

THERE was a loud bang in the laundry building followed by a succession of staccato explosions. "Aunt" Rilda, the laundress, came running from the house to see what was wrong. She opened the door, peered through the smoke, and saw ten-year-old Charlie Thomas looking into a test tube.

"What's happened—are you all right—what's going on here?" she asked in one breath.

"Don't worry, Aunt Rilda," Charlie replied. "This week I'm doing some chemistry experiments. There's bound to be an explosion now and then."

"Why don't you go outdoors and play?" the elderly woman asked. "It's a lot safer there."

Charlie merely shook his head at this suggestion. Wagons and bicycles were all right, in their way, but after school and during the summer months he wanted to explore things, to follow wherever his natural curiosity might lead him.

Born near Lexington, Kentucky, on February 15, 1900, Charles A. Thomas was the son of Frances Carrick Thomas and Charles Allen Thomas. The senior Thomas had come to this country from Melbourne, Australia. He was a minister and died when his only child was an infant.

Charlie's innumerable scientific experiments were not limited to the laundry or the workbench in the cellar of the house. Not long after he startled "aunt" Rilda, his real aunt happened to look out the window and saw her nephew standing on top of the barn roof preparing to take off in a homemade airplane. With difficulty she persuaded him to come down and defer the flight test until another time.

While attending the Morton High School in Lexington, Charlie was a frequent visitor at the chemistry laboratory of nearby Transylvania College. Undoubtedly the interest and friendship of one of the professors influenced his choice of chemistry as his major when he later was an undergraduate at Transylvania.

At college Charlie played football, sang in the choir, made countless friends, and still found enough time for study to be elected to Phi Beta Kappa. To supplement the money which he received from a scholarship, Charlie sang in various Lexington churches and worked on a construction gang during the summer months. It was while at college that he first displayed an unusual ability to explain the most intricate subject in easy-to-understand language, an invaluable asset for any scientist.

From Transylvania he went to Massachusetts Institute of Technology where his early interest in chemistry now became a specialization. Again he helped finance his education by singing with church choirs, this time in Boston. Graduation with an M.S. degree in 1924 brought an offer from General Motors' research laboratory in Dayton, Ohio, where he was assigned a place in the laboratory next to Carroll A. Hochwalt, a recent graduate of the University of Dayton. The two young men became good friends immediately, and spent much time together after work discussing their jobs and ideas for new experiments and products.

Hochwalt was quiet, studious, and soft-spoken, in contrast to his gregarious, redheaded friend Charlie Thomas. Charlie enjoyed nothing better than to be with a crowd, to lead group singing about a piano, or to indulge in an innocent practical joke.

One of Thomas' first assignments was to work on the problem of taking lead out of anti-knock gasoline which contained tetraethyl lead. It was discovered that bromine would eliminate the lead, but because bromine was controlled by the Germans it was in very short supply. This posed a challenge to Thomas who knew that, since the ocean contained this chemical, it would be a logical place to look. His plan was to find the bromine first and then to evolve some method of extracting it. He lost no time visiting several ports on the East Coast where he hired rowboats, rowed from one place to another, sampled seawater and determined the amount of bromine in each bottle. As a result of his discoveries the steamship *Ethyl* was commissioned to extract bromine from seawater, using a technique which involved the employment of chlorine.

That young Thomas had executive as well as scientific ability was demonstrated by the way he managed to get his car painted. After starting work at General Motors he bought a red Buick which was in sore need of a new paint job. Looking about for someone familiar with paints, he found Dick Gaugler, who agreed to select the right shade and help with the job.

"Can you start painting about seven-thirty tonight?" Thomas asked, and his friend nodded in agreement. They began promptly at the appointed time, but a few minutes later Hank DuPont drove up in his new car. Sitting next to him were two of the attractive Talbott sisters.

"You don't mind if I take a short ride with Hank, do

you?" Thomas asked Dick, and he was off, leaving the paint specialist to do the job by himself. This happened more than once, and not only did Thomas get his car repainted but, more important, in 1926 he persuaded Margaret Talbott to become his wife.

Not content with a full day's work in the General Motors laboratory, Thomas and his friend Hochwalt, who was now production manager of the Ethyl Gasoline Corporation, made arrangements with the University of Dayton to use the laboratory evenings. The men were especially interested in developing a chemical extinguisher that would smother gasoline fires. On the basis of this special research they published their first scientific paper, reporting on the effect of alkali metal compounds on combustion. They showed that the elements of the first group of the Periodic Table have a definite negative catalytic effect on the combustion of hydrocarbons, and that even potassium chlorate in water solution will instantly extinguish gasoline flames.

About this time General Motors planned to move its laboratories. Neither Thomas nor his new bride wanted to leave Dayton, however, so he made a proposition to his friend Hochwalt.

"How would you feel about being your own boss and starting an industrial research laboratory with me?"

Hochwalt thought for a few seconds, then his face brightened. "I have it!" he exclaimed. "Let's call it the Thomas and Hochwalt laboratories. We'll do general research and consultant work for the chemical industry."

No sooner had the partners rented the attic of a Dayton office building than the first job, giving the young scientists the task of working on synthetic rubber, came from General Motors. The assignment triggered Thomas' lifelong interest in studying how aluminum chloride worked. He soon became one of the foremost experts on the subject, and later published a comprehensive volume, *Anhydrous Aluminum Chloride in Organic Chemistry*.

The General Motors job was not enough to support the two men and their families and it soon became apparent to Thomas, whose abilities included that of selling, that they would have to seek other customers. As a result, he and Hochwalt would talk and plan far into the night, deciding what *they* would do were they in charge of research for a certain company. The next morning, all fired with enthusiasm, Thomas would rush off to New York or Chicago and call on that company, outline their ideas to the president, and explain how the proposed program would add to the company's profit. Salesman-engineer-administrator Thomas was proficient at whatever he undertook, and their business grew steadily. Projects on which they embarked included making synthetic rubber, perfecting fire extinguishers, working out a procedure for decarbonizing automobiles, and devising a method of aging whiskey quickly. One of their customers was Edgar Monsanto Queeny, president of Monsanto Chemical Company.

Having noted that the Thomas & Hochwalt Laboratory had been successfully launched into the business world and that Charles A. Thomas was awarded a doctor's degree from Transylvania in 1933, let us go back some thirty-odd years to 1901 when a tall, sandy-mustached American of Irish descent was looking about for some means of earning a little extra money during his spare time to help support his growing family.

John Francis Queeny left school at the age of twelve after the great Chicago Fire of 1871 destroyed his father's business. John, the oldest of six children, speedily found a $3-a-week job as a messenger boy for a drug firm. Intelligent and aggressive, he won a succession of promotions and was appointed purchasing agent in 1897 for Meyer Bros. of St. Louis. The previous year he had married Olga Monsanto, the cultured daughter of a Spanish father and a German mother. By 1901 the couple had a son, Edgar Monsanto, and a daughter, Olguita.

In 1899 John Queeny lost his life savings of $6,000 when his first spare-time venture, a factory to grind flowers of sulphur (a substance in powder form, made from condensed vapors), burned to the ground the day it opened for business. Undaunted, he had saved another $1,500 by 1901, and was ready for a second try.

This time he planned to make saccharin, a chemical derived from coal tar, a discovery made at Johns Hopkins in 1879. Saccharin is 500 times sweeter than sugar, is used by diabetics and others who cannot eat sweets, as well as by manufacturers of soft drinks, candy and various foods. At that time the Germans were producing most of the saccharin used in the world, and Meyer Bros. was importing some for resale in this country.

Since John Queeny did not think it right for the purchasing agent of Meyer Bros. to set up a business under his own name, he incorporated the new enterprise as the Monsanto Chemical Company, in honor of his wife. A young Swiss chemist, Dr. Louis Veillon, was hired, an unused section of the Diamond Match Company's warehouse on St. Louis' South Second Street was leased, and necessary new and secondhand machinery was purchased. Within 45 days the company was in business.

As soon as the Germans learned of their new competitor they dropped the price of saccharin from $4.50 to less than

$1 a pound—below the manufacturing cost! This news, added to all his other problems, must have made John Queeny's life a perpetual nightmare. Each day, after finishing his job at Meyer Bros., he went directly to his own plant and worked late into the night. When most men were resting on Sunday after putting in a six-day week, Queeny and Veillon were as busy as ever at the little factory, and for all their effort they chalked up a loss of $1,502 that first year.

There was still worse to come, for the Germans, hoping to put Monsanto out of business altogether, soon opened a plant in New Jersey. Congressmen paid no attention to Queeny's appeals for tariff help to keep the German-made saccharin out of the United States. It seemed that the American chemical industry did not want any tariffs imposed on chemicals, drugs, or dyes which they had to import from Europe. The sugar lobby was also active in fighting Monsanto and trying to eliminate it as a dangerous threat to the sugar processing companies. At the same time Dr. Harvey W. Wiley, of the U. S. Department of Agriculture's Bureau of Chemistry, launched a crusade for pure foods and drugs and chose saccharin as one of his main objects to attack.

No one will ever know why Queeny did not give up— especially in 1904 when Monsanto lost over $2,000 and its working capital had sunk to $204. He became instead more determined to succeed and arranged to bring another chemist from Switzerland, Gaston DuBois. Under DuBois' direction the company branched into the extraction of caffeine from tea waste and prepared to manufacture vanillin, a synthetic vanilla flavoring. At the same time Queeny somehow persuaded friends and business acquaintances to invest another $15,000 in the company.

This proved to be the turning point in the company's

history. The Germans decided that Monsanto had become too strong to fight and relaxed their price war. In 1906 Monsanto made its first profit, $10,000, and in 1907 Queeny quit his job with Meyer Bros. to devote full time to his own company. Until 1914 the years showed slow growth and recurring crises troubled the energetic president, but Queeny kept the company humming and concentrated on building up Monsanto's reputation for quality and integrity.

Gradually he added new products and with the outbreak of World War I in 1914, Monsanto and other American chemical companies were suddenly deluged with orders from both the United States and abroad. Since it was no longer possible to obtain drugs and chemicals from Europe, American manufacturers had to learn how to make their products from basic raw materials. Thus Monsanto research was born of necessity, and in 1915 sales passed the million-dollar mark for the first time.

The end of the war brought a revival of German competition and heavy debts for the company, so that it was not until 1926 that Monsanto again enjoyed satisfactory earnings. The following year John Queeny, whose career was drawing to a close, sold a large block of his Monsanto stock, opening the way to making Monsanto a publicly owned company. Next he turned the presidency of the company over to Edgar Monsanto Queeny, his thirty-year-old son, a man whose vision, financial acumen, and daring were to be largely responsible for the company's continued growth and prosperity during the depression years ahead.

Now the company expanded into new fields—rubber chemicals, food chemicals, plastics, detergents, and many others—by absorbing smaller chemical companies and expanding its own operations. Above all, Mr. Queeny recognized the importance of research, and in 1936, desirous of consolidating the company's research program under expert leadership, acquired the up-and-coming firm of Thomas & Hochwalt. The laboratories became known as the Central Research Department, with Dr. Thomas as director and Dr. Hochwalt the assistant director.

After joining Monsanto, Dr. Thomas carried out important work on the synthesis of styrene, studying all the possible processes and soon concentrating on the method now in use. Under his direction further expansion took place in detergents and resulted in the company's first large-scale plant for those products at Nitro, West Virginia. New lines were developed, particularly in the field of oxidation, and soon the whole organization began to feel the influence of this new man.

Dr. Thomas' active mind shied away from no field that promised to be interesting. It was once said that his interests ranged "from smoked salt for curing of hams and bacon to processes for the production of aliphatic chemicals from hydrocarbon bases." More than a hundred patents were registered in his and Dr. Hochwalt's names, and many of Monsanto's interests in detergents, plastics, hydrocarbon chemistry, synthetic fibers, and atomic energy were encouraged or started by Thomas. Occasionally his personal hobbies led to a company concern or vice versa. His farm in Pike County, Missouri, in which he had long been deeply interested, was a proving ground for many of his ideas on agricultural chemistry, including some of Monsanto's commercial soil conditioners and other agricultural products.

An energetic worker, Dr. Thomas tackled each job with a vigor that often taxed his associates. Endowed with almost boundless energy, he could work late into the night and be at the job early next morning with as much pep and enthusiasm as a man who had slept ten hours. A rapid eater, his fellow workers would often try to keep him talking steadily at meals so that they could keep up with him.

With Dr. Thomas it is not all work, however. His wide range of interests and abilities carries over into leisure hours too. He enjoys fishing, shooting quail and duck, tennis and golf, reading, and singing—whenever a group can be gathered about the piano—symphony and drama when free evenings permit, and family outings when the children are at home. He still indulges in an occasional harmless joke and once taught Blackstone, the famous magician, how to walk away from his own shadow. The trick was done by using a fluorescent zinc sulfide screen.

In 1940 when the English were being pummeled by Hitler's Luftwaffe and expected that the Germans would surely attempt an invasion, the British government made an urgent appeal to Americans for help. Because of his research experience with gasoline, Dr. Thomas was asked if he could suggest some way that stores of petrol could be made useless to the Germans in the event of invasion. He quickly discovered a synthetic resin that would do this, but fortunately it was never needed.

The year 1942 was a memorable one for Dr. Thomas. Of greatest importance was his election to Monsanto's Board of Directors, thus broadening his interest and responsibility as well as making his wide experience and knowledge available to the corporation's top managing board. That same year he was also elected a director of the American Chemical Society and responded to Uncle Sam's call to aid the war effort as a member of the National Defense Research Committee.

Following the crippling blow at Pearl Harbor on December 7, 1941, there was a period of preparation during which our country suffered several serious military setbacks. The outlook was bleak, but even in the darkest hours every American was confident that victory would come as soon as we could get our factories producing enough munitions and our soldiers trained and in the field. Dr. Thomas was assigned the development of fuels for rocket motors. At the same time the scientist was made a member of the Synthetic Rubber Advisory Committee which helped draw up the plan whereby our synthetic rubber industry was founded and regulated.

The following year Dr. Thomas joined the now famous Manhattan District as coordinator. (Manhattan District was the code name for a supersecret project of utmost importance.) Dr. Thomas was responsible for the final purification and metallurgy of plutonium, then a newly discovered element (Number 99) which was essential to the construction of the atom bomb.

During the war years he traveled continually, flying from the East to the West Coast, returning to St. Louis, dashing up to Chicago, on to Washington, back to St. Louis for a few hours of rest, and then off again to another destination. Because of pressing wartime duties he was seldom home to see his wife and family, which then consisted of a fourteen-year-old son and three daughters. While working for the various governmental projects his inexhaustible energy enabled him to remain active at Monsanto and in 1945, when the company took over the management of the Clinton Laboratories, Dr. Thomas was made the project chief. Here, from 1945 to 1948, he directed the first commercial development of radioactive isotopes which have since found their way into the laboratories and hospitals of the world, and a beginning was made on the study of the utilization of atomic energy for power. Little wonder that in 1946

Dr. Thomas was chosen as one of the five members of the important Lilienthal Committee which, after six weeks of intensive work, published a plan for international control of atomic energy. Subsequently almost all the recommendations were incorporated into the international plan advocated by the American Committee for the United Nations.

In recognition of his important contribution to the nation's bomb project, Secretary of War Patterson awarded Dr. Thomas the Medal of Merit. Of all the numerous medals and other honors which have been given him, this is still the most important, for it represents the highest award the United States government can confer on one of its citizens. The citation stated that he "completed vital research and solved production problems of extreme complexity without which the atomic bomb could not have been."

With the successful conclusion of the war in 1945, Dr. Thomas was elected vice-president and a member of the Executive Committee as well as technical director of Monsanto, and two years later its executive vice-president. The latter promotion represented his final break from the laboratory to the office, from the role of scientist to that of administrator. No longer surrounded by Bunsen burners, beakers, flasks, complicated electronic equipment and other laboratory paraphernalia, he was now in a world of paper, telephone calls, conferences and management decisions.

As technical director of the company, it was his job to develop new ways of coordinating all of the various research activities that were being carried out in the many different divisions of the company. This required holding quarterly meetings with the various research directors and the heads of technical departments, often spending a whole day going over each of their problems, one by one, analyzing proposals, answering questions, making suggestions and finding out where he could be of help in achieving the end result which the director was seeking. Dr. Thomas never failed to attend annual meetings of the company's research directors where new fields of activity were mapped out and more difficult problems of research management discussed. It was his regular practice to visit the laboratories where he would make a point of singling out individual researchers and group leaders for informal chats or join a little knot of men as they took time off for a cup of coffee.

To enable his men to keep abreast of the latest scientific developments, he introduced a program whereby each year a few employees were sent back to universities of their own choice for graduate work. Another idea of his was what he liked to call the "retreat plan." This proposed that a group of technical men be set aside periodically from their present duties and definitely from all interruptions, just to talk and discuss scientific matters in the hope of developing new ideas. Many companies have since adopted this technique— calling it brainstorming.

On May 1, 1951, Dr. Thomas became the company's fifth president and the first technical man to occupy the top administrative spot. In addition to his unique administrative ability he had been widely recognized as one of the nation's leading scientists and had the distinction of being one of the few men whose name was preceded by a star in the biographical volume *American Men of Science*, indicating outstanding achievement.

During the ten years that Dr. Thomas served as president, the company's sales more than tripled in volume, soaring from $272,000,000 to $932,000,000. The newly formed Overseas Division reached out into all parts of the globe while here in the United States the company's list of products grew constantly through intensive research and development until it covered most of the chemical spectrum and placed Monsanto among the very top chemical companies of the world. Still believing that research is basic to the progress of every company, Dr. Thomas, during the year that he moved up from president to chairman of the board, had the satisfaction of seeing the new large-scale research center open in October 1961. This was a project which had been started under his direction, and as he participated in the dedication ceremony he must have thought back thirty-five years to that day when he and Carroll Hochwalt opened their own research consulting business in a downtown Dayton attic.

People stand at the top of Dr. Thomas' interests. The dignity, happiness and career goal of each individual working for the company have always been of importance and concern to him. He has also been long aware that in any company there is bound to be some dissatisfaction but that it can be minimized with intelligent planning.

"The chemistry of the individual chemist becomes a matter of the greatest importance to us," he once said. "You might be interested in knowing what we are doing at Monsanto. We are attempting to ease the stresses between the individual and the corporate organization. I know that this is a matter of general concern throughout the industry.

"We have one laboratory in St. Louis which is guided by principles rather than by rules. Laboratory management reserves the right to determine *what* is to be done. The individual scientists are completely responsible for determining *how* it is to be done. The laboratory has no fixed working hours. Every researcher has a key to it. In the interest of personal safety, we have an open communications system between the laboratories and a guard station which is manned twenty-four hours a day. Anyone in trouble can call for assistance at any hour.

"To offset the traditional complaint of the scientist that no one in management can understand what he is saying, we have established a recognized and practicing scientist as an outrider to departmental top management. He is available to all parties whenever the need for translation or interpretation becomes apparent. We have removed some irritation by assigning group leaders autonomy and authority to handle most of the issues brought to their attention.

In this same laboratory, on an experimental basis, we have a standing offer for the creative individual: Up to two years off from regular assignments to work on his big new idea! All he has to do is convince his superiors of the validity of the project and set an appropriate time limit. I am glad to say we have already had a few takers on this offer. We hope to have more in the future.

"The corporation's need to make a profit complements the desire of the scientist and the engineer to achieve distinction, and out of this partnership society has received the gift of progress."

Scientist, administrator, husband, parent, patriot, humanist—Dr. Thomas has become an example of the technical statesman of the future. Truly a man of many parts, he is an outstanding scientist who, because of his broad outlook on life, has made a rich and varied contribution to human progress.

•

Chapter 2

THE MAN WHO NEEDS NO SLEEP

THE young man sitting at the telephone switchboard expertly plugged the long black cords into the hole-studded panel on the wire chief's console.

"An all-over busy signal on position 17? Okay, I'll be right up to fix it."

It was two-thirty in the morning and the tall, good-looking youth was as wide awake and alert as through he had just awakened from eight hours' sleep. Known to his friends as "the man who needs no sleep," Larry Hafstad, doing his regular 11 P.M. to 7 A.M. shift for the telephone company, was earning his expenses while attending the University of Minnesota.

Born on June 18, 1904, in Minneapolis, Minnesota, Lawrence Randolph Hafstad was the son of Ellen Bruem and Bernt Andrew Hafstad. We know little about his boyhood except that he lived on the south side of Minneapolis where he attended grade and high schools. The family did not have the means to give him further education, so he resolved to put himself through college. Upon graduation from high school he went to work for the Northwestern Bell Telephone Company as a linesman, and this led to his job in

Central Office maintenance on the evening or night shift in the Cherry Exchange.

While Larry was a freshman he met Merle Tuve, a senior who worked in the same telephone office. The two became good friends and there grew between them a close association that was to last for many years. Another Minnesota student of that day was Lloyd V. Berkner, somewhat younger, whom Larry later taught when he was a laboratory instructor. The careers of all three men were closely allied through their postgraduate years, to the scientific benefit of the nation. Dr. Tuve became director of the Department of Terrestrial Magnetism of Carnegie Institution, and Dr. Berkner was appointed president of Associated Universities, Inc., which operates the Brookhaven National Laboratory on Long Island.

"Level-headed Larry," as Hafstad was also called, made excellent grades during college and received his B.S. in electrical engineering in 1926. While working for the telephone company there were many things about electricity that aroused his curiosity. He observed that physicists could answer such questions better than anyone else, and decided to become one. He therefore continued his studies at the university for two additional years, concentrating in the field of physics. While attending graduate school he advanced from the position of maintenance man to that of engineer at the telephone company.

Having completed the work for his master's degree at Minnesota, Hafstad accepted a position as associate physicist for the Carnegie Institution of Washington, D.C., and, true to his reputation for needing little sleep, also studied for his doctorate at Johns Hopkins in nearby Baltimore. He earned his Ph.D. in 1933, nuclear physics being the subject of his thesis, and that same year he advanced to the position of physicist with the Carnegie Institution, a post he held until 1942. Noted for being a wonderful teacher, Hafstad had a gift for making complex things simple. This trait was to prove extremely valuable in later years. In 1945 for instance, as soon as the secret of the atom bomb was out after Hiroshima, he conducted, with Professor George Gamow, a lecture course to give an understanding of nuclear physics to naval officers. Later he was called upon to explain atomic energy matters to Budget Bureau officials and Congressmen in getting support for the Nautilus submarine program.

In his laboratory days Hafstad was involved in a variety of research projects. Perhaps one of the more noteworthy studies was that concerning the propagation of radio waves. With his old friend Dr. Merle Tuve and another scientist, he investigated the upper atmosphere, or ionosphere, measuring the height and distance of its radio-reflecting layer and its relation to magnetic storms. These findings later proved valuable in the development of radar.

In 1931 he and Dr. Tuve received the American Association for the Advancement of Science award for developing a one-million-volt X-ray tube, a forerunner of the now popular accelerators, which would provide information about the behavior of nuclear particles.

During the 1930's Dr. Hafstad was one of the early workers in nuclear disintegration experiments and was actively involved in some of the now classical proton-proton scattering work. In 1939 he, together with R. B. Roberts and R. C. Meyer, bombarded uranium with atomic particles to verify European reports that German scientists had split the atomic nuclei and that energy could be released in that way. Theirs was one of several simultaneous United States experiments in this particular field which led the way to the development of the atom bomb. Shortly thereafter the same group reported its first observations on delayed neutron emission in the fission process, which later became so important in reactor control.

In 1940, while still at Carnegie Institution, Dr. Hafstad began defense research under Dr. Vannevar Bush, in the earliest stages of the National Defense Research Committee program, a program which eventually became the government's Office of Scientific Research & Development. With characteristic enthusiasm and his ability to work around the clock with little sleep, he plunged into the hectic wartime tasks assigned him by a government that desperately needed the best scientific help available. There was so much to do and so little time to get it done. Frantic appeals for help came from all directions; projects ranged from ordnance to ramjet engines, missile guidance systems to torpedo fuzes.

It was this last assignment which led to perhaps the most important development, that of the proximity fuze (with his old friend Dr. Tuve) and the establishment of the Applied Physics Laboratory of Johns Hopkins University not only for the purpose of developing it, but to monitor its production and use. According to a scientist who knew Dr. Hafstad's work intimately, "he was an excellent balance wheel among some prima donna scientists in the Applied Physics Laboratory of Johns Hopkins University during the war years."

The need for a proximity fuze had been evident for some time, especially in connection with antiaircraft gunnery. Up to then, all antiaircraft shells contained a time fuze which the gunner set before firing. It was difficult to judge the exact number of seconds that would be required for a shell to reach its target. If it exploded too soon or too late, it was wasted. Similarly, when firing against ground targets, if the explosion occurred too soon or after it had imbedded itself deep into the ground, it could be equally ineffective. The proximity fuze that replaced the former time fuze contained a tiny radio transmitter and receiver. The radio transmitted toward the target signals which were reflected and picked up by the receiver as the shell sped through the air. Once the strength of the signals indicated that the shell was within a predetermined distance of the target, the fuze automatically detonated the shell. It has been stated that this invention greatly helped our soldiers win the crucial Battle of the Bulge, giving the Allied forces a distinct advantage over the Nazis, who had tried to make such a device but failed.

"Dr. Hafstad was not exactly an aggressive leader," a former colleague asserted. "He was more of an excellent adviser and inspirational guide. He knew how to promote teamwork, even among strong-minded individuals; he gave responsible persons plenty of authority; he wasn't bothered with routine reports but insisted on knowing important developments and had a knack for welding them together."

The Secretary of the Navy awarded Dr. Hafstad the Medal of Merit in 1946 for the brilliant assistance he had given in the development of various ordnance devices for the Army and Navy, and during that same year he received the King's Medal in Defense of Freedom from the British government.

As one of the pioneer researchers in the field, it was no surprise when, immediately after World War II, Dr. Hafstad was appointed executive secretary of the Department of Defense's Research & Development Board, under the chairmanship of Dr. Vannevar Bush. The formation of this board recognized the continuing need for the close coordination between the scientific community and the government which had prevailed during the war, and which was to become a standard and vital aspect of our national defense preparations.

Dr. Hafstad's next research adventure started when he was discussing his coordination problems and frustrations in the Pentagon with his friend Admiral Mills, then chief of the Bureau of Ships and a member of RDB. Like Dr. Hafstad, he had long been interested in the possibility of a nuclear-powered submarine. The Admiral urged Hafstad to take on this job in the then newly created but as yet unfilled position of Director of Reactor Development in the Atomic Energy Commission, and promised maximum cooperation from the Navy as an inducement. As a team, they ran interference for Admiral Rickover, obtained and gave the necessary approvals and backing, and, in short, made possible the development of our nuclear submarines. This was the beginning, for Dr. Hafstad, of a six-year tour of duty in the Atomic Energy Commission. For his work with the Commission he received the AEC's Distinguished Service Award.

In addition to his military assignment Dr. Hafstad was interested in making nuclear energy available for peacetime uses, although he was more aware than many of his associates of the important economic hurdle for nuclear civilian power reactors. Looking ahead many years to a time when the world would need tremendous amounts of energy because some existing sources would become exhausted, he foresaw a day some time in the future when nuclear power might be the best source of inexpensive energy.

Dr. Hafstad has pointed out that in our modern society we have learned how to use energy to replace human labor. The human is used for his brain, and energy, in various forms, is used in place of muscle. We seldom realize the amount of energy we use—or think about its equivalent in "servants"—for example. A one-horsepower electric motor does in effect as much work as ten men. This is what we assume as the ratio between horsepower and human labor. Thus when you flick on a fan which has a one-tenth-horse-power motor, one servant fans the breeze for you. When you turn on the oil-fired furnace, the one-third-horsepower pump represents three or four servants shoveling coal. Today all modern nations are using something like five or more horsepower per individual, and since our standard of living is based on the availability of large amounts of energy, how long will our sources of energy last?

Reserves of fluid fuels, oil and gas, are not unlimited. Near the end of this century it is anticipated that their price will start to rise, but that at the same time other fuels will come into the picture. Chemists will then very likely convert coal into gasoline so that we can continue to run our automobiles, trains, planes, tractors, and other devices that cannot burn coal. But if we still need more energy and if we ever run out of coal, we can get as much as we like from uranium. The only trouble is that so far the price of energy produced from that source has been unduly high.

But two things are happening. The price of atomic energy is beginning to come down while the price of other energy sources is bound to go up gradually. When the price of atomic energy becomes competitive it will begin to be used, and every day scientists and engineers are working on devices which will make atomic energy cheaper.

On January 1, 1955, Dr. Hafstad became director of the Chase Manhattan Bank's Atomic Energy Division in New York City and represented the bank at conferences with industrialists and others who were planning private industrial development of atomic energy. If this switch from the laboratory and administrative office to a bank seems odd, it must be remembered that before corporations can plan and build nuclear energy plants they must obtain money to finance the work. Few bankers know much about atomic energy, hence it was a wise move on the part of the Chase Manhattan Bank to hire Dr. Hafstad to head its Atomic Energy Division.

After this jump from government into business he made one more move in September of that year, this time succeeding Charles L. McCuen as General Motors vice-president in charge of the Research Laboratories. Let Dr. Hafstad tell you himself about General Motors and its vast research program.

"General Motors is a decentralized organization. The various operating divisions—Buick, Cadillac, Frigidaire, Electro-Motive and others—are autonomous. They have their own complete organizations so they can do as much research as they like—or feel they can afford. We do not control their research from a central laboratory. The work going on here at the Technical Center is in addition to the engineering and research in the various divisions.

"At the Technical Center we have Research Laboratories, Engineering Staff, Styling Staff, and Manufacturing Development. Each of these four staff organizations is independent and each reports to the president of General Motors.

"You might be interested to know how the work is divided. I would put it something like this: In the divisions under day-to-day commercial pressures the future lead time is three years. This is the nature of the automotive business with complicated model changes that are a long time getting into production. Ordinarily the men in the automotive divisions project their thinking and activities three years ahead—if they are to stay in the automobile business.

"The Engineering Staff, Mr. Charles A. Chayne's organization, overlaps this three-year cycle somewhat. I would say he and his men work from three to six years (or thereabouts) in the future. We in Research Laboratories should take over and go still farther out into the blue. We should cover what might be of interest to the corporation at some indefinite future time, possibly a time range from five to fifteen years, depending on how good our crystal ball is. If we looked further into the future, we would. But it is pretty hard looking forward ten or fifteen years.

"To emphasize this, I would ask you for a moment to look back fifteen years and visualize everything as it was then. What kind of dreaming would you have to do to visualize everything as it is now? Moreover, everything moves faster now than fifteen years ago, so changes in the next fifteen years are going to be greater than they were in the past fifteen years.

"Probably you are curious as to what we do in the Research Laboratories as well as in the other organizations at the Technical Center. Certainly I will not try to explain everything. I perhaps might say that in the Engineering Staff, as you would expect, they are working on new types of cars, new devices to go into cars. By and large, it is a hardware operation.

"We at the Research Laboratories try to go further into the future and get more into the scientific work, but only in those areas of interest and importance to General Motors. For example, we are looking at the gas turbine to see if it is practicable in automobiles. We look at other types of unconventional engines—free piston engines, rotary engines—plus many things which might conceivably be used in automobiles. We try to determine what their advantages are and whether their development should be accelerated.

"We cover various fields of science. We have physics departments, chemistry departments, plastics departments and so on, each following experiments that would be of interest in any one of the many General Motors divisions. It might be well here to emphasize the wide variety of activities in an organization as large as General Motors. We have not only the automobile business, but also the Frigidaire activity and the household appliance divisions which have entirely different problems than the automotive people. Beyond that we have Electro-Motive which builds big railroad locomotives, with another category of problems. So you see we have a truly wide range of technical problems to deal with.

"Also, we try to help with what are called trouble-shooting problems when the divisions get into production or service difficulties. This is one of the Research Laboratories' functions—to have people available as consultants to help solve these problems.

"What are considered the more 'futuristic' activities in science, and which of these do we in the Research Laboratories consider the most challenging?

"Perhaps the biggest revolution is the introduction of computer technology. You have heard of electronic brains. We use these, naturally, and have used them a long time in bookkeeping operations. They are now and for some time have been moving into engineering, design and production activities. I don't know how well you are acquainted with electronic computers but they are fascinating and developments with them are really staggering. It is often said, and I think it is true, that the electronic computer is likely to do for man's brain what the steam engine did for his muscles.

"To give you some idea of the scale at which these computers now are operating, the original smaller ones (now generally used in bookkeeping) would handle something like 1,000 operations per second. This would be 1,000 additions, subtractions, multiplications or functions of that kind. Current computers, more or less standard in engineering work, operate in the neighborhood of 15,000 computations per second. We have installed a new computer because 15,000 computations per second wasn't fast enough. The new one will be operating at approximately 100,000 computations per second.

"This opens up an entirely new approach to technical problems. With these devices we can set up programs so that in principle we can design several mechanisms—several machines, if you like—and then try out one design after another to determine which is best and most efficient.

"In the old days you never could afford to build several variations or versions of a machine to find out which was best. But this computer technique goes on continuously. We don't know what end is in sight and it will be interesting to see how far we can go.

"What about other areas that are exciting at this time? Well, energy conversion is receiving an enormous amount of attention. You have all read so much about atomic energy that I won't spend much time on it. There are approaches to this energy conversion problem, however, which we refer to as the direct conversion technique or, in this case, going directly from heat to electricity.

"In our big electrical plants you go from coal or oil to a combustion process to make steam to drive a turbine which drives a generator that produces electricity. If we can get direct conversion from heat to electricity we can obtain more efficiency and lower the cost of electricity. This is especially true of atomic energy, where the conversion process is particularly expensive.

"Heat is very cheap if you get it from atomic energy. It is cheap anyway but from atomic energy it would be extremely cheap if we could solve the problem of getting from heat to electrical energy. Several approaches are being explored. There is the thermoelectric approach of heating dissimilar metals joined together and getting electricity from the junction. At the moment this is not quite so promising as it was thought to be a few years ago.

"Another idea is to use heat to bring to a high temperature an emitter which emits electrons, just as the filament of the vacuum tube does, and you collect these electrons. In effect, you have a miniature battery—actually a vacuum tube which acts like a battery. This still has considerable promise as a way of getting from heat to electricity directly. One reason it is being pushed is that it would be ideal power in a submarine because it would do away with all rotating machinery and the noise that goes with it. That is why the government is pouring a lot of money into this process and if successful it will have a revolutionary effect.

"Another interesting energy conversion technique is the fuel cell. Dry cells, as we know them, are pretty effective for flashlights and other things but they are always running down. Just when you want the flashlight the battery is dead.

"The fuel cell's advantage is that you could have a fuel supply and the battery would operate in a way that you would burn this fuel only when you are using the cell. So your flashlight would keep the reacting chemical elements separate until you wanted to use it. Then you would connect them and get electricity as you needed it.

"What is exciting is that in such a chemical reaction you can get up to 75 or 80 percent efficiency. The maximum efficiency of a heat engine will be around 40 percent because of temperature limitations. In chemical reactions you don't have such limitations. You would be able almost to double the efficiency of a chemical energy conversion device. This is an exciting prospect and researchers are looking very hard at it. At present the reactions have been carried out but the apparatus is much too bulky to be of practical interest. But virtually all new developments go through that stage.

"One more item might be of interest, the Laser. It is a close relative to the Maser which was developed in connection with radar and microwave techniques. The Laser does much the same sort of thing but at frequencies of ordinary light.

"This is a very abstruse sort of thing. I would describe it this way: You know how the beam of an ordinary flashlight or searchlight shines out into space. The beam gradually spreads out and the intensity drops. Anyone who has tried using a searchlight has often said to himself, 'Wouldn't it be nice if all this energy would stay in a nice parallel beam so it would go any distance without decreasing in intensity and spreading out and getting lost?'

"The Laser does exactly this. It is a very exciting concept. If you have a flashlight or a searchlight here on earth, let us say, and you use a Laser, all the light leaving that searchlight would land on about a mile or two-mile surface of the moon. This is how strong this particular beam is.

"Offhand this seems like an amusing trick for the scientist to play, but it has a lot of implications. If you were to set up a number of these Lasers across the country you could start with a very sharply defined beam for an enormous distance and transmit information over these channels such as you now do over wires.

"This is one of its implications. Another is that in effect you can transmit energy through space, which is something we have been dreaming about a long time, because all the energy leaving the searchlight lands with very little loss at the far end. It is going to be important with the satellite business. Suppose we have a satellite circling above the earth somewhere and want to communicate with it. The Laser would permit us to focus our signals on this very small satellite and get the signals back as a reflection."

Under Dr. Hafstad's direction General Motors is gradually getting back into defense research after dropping from the fifth largest government research contractor in 1951 to sixteenth in 1961. Inasmuch as it appears that the government will be spending $17 or $18 billion for research by 1970, General Motors will gradually increase its research interests and take what Dr. Hafstad has described as a "middle of the road position."

"We are looking for the small tough job whose solution is a real contribution," Dr. Hafstad said, explaining the management's decision to do pieces of research instead of bidding for the management of huge prime contracts.

It would seem likely that responsibilities stemming from this new program will keep "the man who needs no sleep" awake long hours as he ponders the many problems that come to the director of a research organization.

As it steps up its research program, one of the most difficult problems facing General Motors is finding the technical men who will measure up to the exacting standards Dr. Hafstad has set for his staff. What he wants are scientists and research engineers, not handbook engineers. He is not interested in hiring men who want to work on a concept that has already been worked out. Instead, the scientists he hires must be original thinkers, capable of creating concepts.

What is this man like?

Dr. Hafstad has been described as a rather shy, retiring man, who could walk any avenue of public relations and do an outstanding job—whether it be a speech, a magazine article, an interview, or whatnot—just so long as he did not have to talk about himself. Even close friends do not know intimate details about his personal life except that he married Mary Cowen (they have one son, William A. Hafstad); that he likes to skate and ski in winter and garden and canoe in summer; that he is a weekend farmer and likes to work with his hands.

The year Dr. Hafstad made a trip around the world under the auspices of Atoms for Peace, Inc., he proved himself "amazingly successful" as an ambassador of goodwill for the United States. His sympathetic understanding as a teacher and counselor as well as his tact and diplomacy were reported as serving our country in good stead in helping prepare the way for our participation in the International Conference on the Peaceful Uses of Atomic Energy at Geneva, Switzerland.

As we look back over Dr. Hafstad's professional career, it seems both logical and provident that he should have crowned his brilliant lifetime work by lending his talents to private industry. In our free enterprise system the corporation is responsible for undertaking most government research and manufacturing contracts. With General Motors performing increasingly important research functions for the federal government, Dr. Hafstad is in a position where he can best serve our nation as he directs the General Motors Research Laboratories in vital work which he loves and knows so well.

•

Chapter 3

THE VERSATILE SCIENTIST

THERE is not a man, woman, or child in the United States whose eating habits and diet have not been influenced by a kindly, unassuming man who has spent a lifetime studying nutrition and searching for ways to preserve and improve the food we eat. Food—of which frozen items comprise a substantial part—is a $75 billion a year business. Probably the man who knows more about frozen foods than anyone else in the country, if not in the world, is Dr. Donald K. Tressler, scientist-researcher-author-lecturer-nutritionist-publisher-patriot, who lives and works in Westport, Connecticut.

Donald K. Tressler was born on November 7, 1894, in Cincinnati, Ohio. He was the son of Florence Mereness and the Reverend Martin Luther Tressler. His father was a Presbyterian minister whose farmer-blacksmith great-grandfather had immigrated as a young boy to the United States from Germany in 1746. As was the case with so many ministers' families, the Tresslers moved frequently from one parish to another, so Donald received his early education in various public schools in Indiana and Ohio. In spite of changing schools so often—or perhaps because of it—

Donald proved an exceptional student and entered Miami University at Oxford, Ohio, when he was still fourteen.

The young freshman had long known what he wanted to study at college. As a hobby his father was especially intrested in agricultural chemistry and scientific methods of raising foods, and at one time owned two farms where he conducted experiments in these fields. In his study were some 500 books on scientific agriculture. One of the volumes, a chemistry text, fascinated Donald, who was studying physics in high school at the time. By coincidence his teacher knew more about chemistry than physics. Because of what the instructor told the class plus what he read in his father's study, Donald decided to pursue the subject as a lifetime career. At home he set up a laboratory in a spare room and evolved a plan for majoring in chemistry at college, after which he would go to Germany and take his doctorate there. The outbreak of World War I was to change all this.

At the beginning of his sophomore year Donald transferred to the University of Michigan at Ann Arbor to be nearer his family, which had moved again. At Michigan he took all of the food and chemistry courses offered, and when he graduated in 1913 with an A.B. he went to work for the Pennsylvania Salt Manufacturing Company as a scientific chemist. Two months later he received an urgent call from the superintendent of the Flint, Michigan, schools.

"Mr. Tressler," the official said, "would you consider teaching chemistry in our high school?"

"I have a job here," the young scientist said.

"I know—but we're in an awful fix. Our chemistry teacher can't return this fall, so I contacted the university and they recommended you very highly. Won't you help us out?"

Tressler had no idea of teaching school but the prospect interested him, and also he wanted to be of help.

"I'll take it for one year," he promised, "then I'm going back to college to work for my doctorate."

The following fall he had enrolled at Ohio State University when a telegram arrived from Cornell.

URGENTLY NEED YOUR SERVICE AS INSTRUCTOR IN CHEMISTRY. TELEPHONE COLLEGE AND WE WILL DISCUSS DETAILS.

Thanks to his teaching experience at Flint and the high recommendation of the University of Michigan, the university officials at Cornell considered Tressler qualified for the post. The young man accepted the offer and during the next three years studied for his doctorate and earned his living and tuition expenses as an assistant instructor in chemistry.

With the declaration of war in 1917 between the United States and Germany, Tressler wanted to be of real service to his country. It looked as though the best way would be to accept a teaching assignment at Oregon State College and instruct classes in agriculture and food chemistry. By this time his interest in chemistry had narrowed somewhat into nutrition.

Meanwhile the German U-boats that were prowling the North Atlantic were sinking far too many freighters and our experts began to fear that a food shortage might develop. Since fish was plentiful and could become a diet mainstay, the United States Bureau of Fisheries was instructed to step up its studies of fish preservation. Seeing this as a job of vital importance to the country, Tressler accepted a position as research assistant with the Bureau, where he worked under the direction of two members of the National Research Council and Dr. Elmer V. McCollum, the famous vitamin scientist. At the same time he somehow managed to fulfill the remaining requirements for his doctorate at Cornell.

At first Dr. Tressler had to learn all that was then known about salting and preserving fish. He found that hardly any fish was canned but that most of the big catches were salted or smoked to preserve them. What was needed most was a process for salting fish during the hot summer months. In the course of his work he traveled to Florida, then up the coast to North Carolina, Virginia, and on to Maryland.

Not only did Dr. Tressler solve the problem of preserving fish, but even more important, he found himself a wife. While working for five months in the Johns Hopkins School of Hygiene and Public Health, a friend introduced him to numerous people in Baltimore. One of the prettier young ladies whom he met was Ella Watkins, a graduate of the Maryland Institute. There was enough time for the couple to become sufficiently well acquainted for him to propose, and they were married the following spring.

The year 1920 was a memorable one for Dr. Tressler. He was twenty-six, he had acquired a wife, and he had achieved a certain amount of prestige as an instructor and a researcher. Thanks to his knowledge of fishery products, he was hired by the Mellon Institute and assigned the task of making some substitute for the fish which the LePage Company had been using to make its glue. Fish skins were becoming scarce as more and more fish was being refrigerated instead of salted, now that the war was over. At the same time there was an increasing demand for more glue, so that LePage had to seek another source for its raw material. One condition was that the new product be indistinguishable from the regular product which the public had come to accept.

Dr. Tressler tackled the problem, using animal stock to make a hard glue, but this proved quite different from LePage's flowing liquid. Next he tried working with hide fleshings, the soft flesh next to the hide, and after much experimentation found that this made a perfect substitute. LePage's Liquid Glue and the glue process which he invented have been used continuously by the company since that time.

Today the three most important food flavorings are salt, pepper, and M.S.G., or monosodium glutamate. While at the Mellon Institute Dr. Tressler discovered a new source for this substance. The processing of beet molasses, by which it is possible to recover more sugar, is called the "Steffens process." Taking the waste water (Steffens filtrate), Dr. Tressler worked out a method whereby M.S.G. could be manufactured from this otherwise waste material.

Monosodium glutamate is a white substance which has profound flavoring properties and is used both commercially and in home kitchens to emphasize the natural flavoring of foods. In addition to finding a new source for this substance Dr. Tressler developed many unique uses for it, and a company was formed by International Minerals and Metal Co. to manufacture and market the product under the brand name of Ac'cent.

In 1929 Clarence Birdseye invited Dr. Tressler to join his firm. Birdseye had built a small plant at Gloucester, Massachusetts, where he was freezing fish pellets for which he had found a ready market.

"If frozen fish sells well," he told Dr. Tressler, "think of the opportunities waiting for freezing fruits, vegetables, meats and other foods!" The prospect fascinated Dr. Tressler, and soon, under his direction and leadership, frozen peas were coming from a plant in Albion, New York, lima beans from Bridgeton, New Jersey, green beans from Mt. Morris, New York, and blueberries from "down Maine."

Dr. Tressler worked out each freezing process in the laboratory and then approached a cannery which had already indicated interest in getting into the frozen food business. Next he helped the cannery obtain the necessary equipment and worked with the management until all production problems were resolved. He went from plant to plant contracting for new products and expanding the variety of frozen foods until Birdseye became almost a household word.

Meanwhile the depression had deepened, and Dr. Tressler became concerned lest General Foods, which owned the Birdseye business, might have to close the laboratory. At a time when 12,000,000 were unemployed, he received not one, but three job offers. After carefully weighing the pros and cons of each, he chose the position that made him head of the Chemistry Division of the New York State Agricultural Experimental Station as well as professor of agriculture and food chemistry at Cornell University. Here, he reasoned, would be opportunity to tackle not just frozen food research but a wide variety of other projects involving nutrition.

One problem that came to his attention concerned Concord grapes, which sold for only $20 a ton as contrasted to $120 a ton for other varieties. Concord grapes have too strong a flavor ("foxy," they call it) to be useful to the average winery. It was not long before Dr. Tressler had licked the problem and obtained two patents covering the manufacture and rapid aging of sherry and port from Concord grapes. These processes are now in use in the principle wineries in New York State and Ontario, Canada.

Next he directed studies of the vitamin content of foods and vegetables, the effect of processing on vitamins, fermentation of sparkling cider, dehydration of vegetables and fruits, and the development of chemical methods for determining ascorbic acid, carotene and thiamin. However, his chief accomplisments were in the frozen food field.

More than anyone else Dr. Tressler was responsible for the popularity of home freezers. He studied the bacteriology of frozen foods to make certain that home freezing was safe. Many people thought that if foods were improperly frozen they would become poisonous, but Dr. Tressler found no such evidence. He gave dozens of lectures, wrote numerous papers, and published a book with C. F. Evers entitled *The Freezing, Preservation of Fruits, Fruit Juices and Vegetables.*

"If food spoils, the housewife knows it," Dr. Tressler declared. "She has far more sense than she is given credit for." One bulletin on home freezing which he wrote for the service enjoyed an extremely wide distribution and undoubtedly influenced and speeded up the sale and use of home freezers.

It was only logical that industry would want to tap the abilities of such a man, and this time it was General Electric's Household Appliance Division at Bridgeport, Connecticut, which beckoned. Dr. Tressler worked out an arrangement whereby he acted as a consultant and was permitted to work for other companies as well. He moved his family, which now consisted of a daughter, Eleanor, and a son, Wilfred, to Westport, Connecticut, where he bought a gracious home with four acres of land. He immediately remodeled the extensive basement into a modern combination laboratory-testing kitchen complete with a huge walk-in icebox and frozen food lockers.

For two years he was manager of General Electric's Consumer Institute in charge of all home economists and the food laboratory at Bridgeport. Meanwhile he conducted research in such diverse technological areas as manufacturing of cake and other dry mixes, use of dehydrated fruits, improvement of photo-offset coatings, the utilization of food by-products, and the manufacture of cream topping. The numerous companies for which he did research included such top names as A. E. Staley Mfg. Co., Canada Packers, Frozen Food Foundation, International Minerals and Metal Co., Merck & Co., Pepperidge Farms, Inc., Reynolds Metals Co., Standard Brands, Inc., and Welch Grape Juice Co.

When the Korean War broke out, Dr. A. Stuart Hunter, a scientist for the Quartermaster Food and Container Institute of the Armed Services, and Dr. Glenn King, then director of the Nutrition Foundation and president of the American Public Health Association, begged Dr. Tressler to come to Chicago to head up the Institute. His expert guidance and knowledge were sought, for it was feared that the war might become a global conflict. "But I have commitments here," the food scientist protested. "I just can't suddenly dump all my clients."

"Couldn't someone run your business for you while you're gone?" was the next question, and that is how Dr. Tressler solved his dilemma. He contacted an old friend, Mr. Karl B. Norton, who had been his assistant at Birdseye, and asked him to move into his home, use the laboratory and carry on the consulting business.

In his new position as Scientific Director, Dr. Tressler administered numerous investigations to improve rations and ration items for the Army, Navy, Marines and Air

Force. He also directed studies of packaging and containers for subsistence items for the armed forces and assisted in bettering the containers, packaging and packing of all Quartermaster items.

While he was still in Chicago, the owner of the Avi Publishing Company, which had brought out five of Dr. Tressler's books, decided to sell the business. When Dr. Tressler learned of this in 1956 he decided to purchase the company, provided he could persuade his friend Mr. Gerald A. Fitzgerald and his wife to run the firm from Westport in his absence. The Fitzgeralds said "yes," but Dr. Tressler gradually became so involved in the affairs of the new company that in 1958 he was compelled to resign his job at Chicago.

Once back in Westport, Dr. Tressler found that he was spending almost two-thirds of his time in the publishing business and the balance on consulting jobs. As editor, publisher, and owner of the firm, he chose from the many manuscripts submitted those which he would publish. He edited each book, designed its format, did the proofreading, and directed the promotion. His staff, consisting of four women, handled all the other details of the business. In 1962 the extensive catalogue of books dealing with all aspects of food included 21 volumes issued by Avi Publishing Company. One of the latest, *Israeli Cookery,* resulted from a trip Dr. Tressler had made to Israel in 1960 for the Technical Aid Program to help the people there start a frozen food industry and learn how to dehydrate food. While working with Lilian Cornfeld, the country's leading nutritional consultant, Dr. Tressler suggested that she write such a book.

When I visited with Dr. Tressler he had, in addition to his publishing venture, various consulting assignments, assisted by a part-time home economist. Among other projects they were doing research on frozen foods for a major airline, working on precooked frozen crab and crab flake dishes for the leading crab fishery, precooked fishery products for a Norwegian packer, helping plan precooked frozen dishes for a large commissary that serves meals in some 200 factories, and assisting a major hotel chain improve its menu planning and methods of food preparation.

Dr. Tressler's other activities have included serving two or three days a month as a consultant to the Office of Civil Defense in Battle Creek, Michigan, where he helped with the selection and preparation of the proper foods for use in shelters. He has aided the chefs at the Culinary Institute of America in learning how to freeze precooked foods, modify recipes, and plan tasty and nutritional dishes. He is an active member of numerous scientific and technical societies including the Institute of Food Technologists (of which he was a founder), the American Chemical Society, the American Public Health Association, and the American Society of Heating and Refrigerating Engineers.

In spite of all the interests and obligations which keep Dr. Tressler extremely busy, he still finds time for his chief hobby—his garden. With characteristic modesty he led us about the acre and a half where he grows some 30 vegetables and seemingly as many varieties of fruits and berries. The garden was as neat and clean as his laboratory, and Dr. Tressler admitted that he did the work himself except for the rows of colorful flowers.

"That's Mrs. Tressler's department," he was careful to point out.

"But what do you do during the winter when you can't garden?" I inquired.

There was a twinkle in his eye as he looked up. "That's

when I have time for my other hobbies—lecturing and writing," he replied.

As long as Dr. Tressler and his associates conduct food research in his well-equipped laboratory, it is quite probable that the American public will continue to enjoy further innovations and improvements in its diet. Most of the frozen foods that jam the grocer's deep freeze and the dry packaged foods that crowd his shelves would never have been processed and packed were it not for the knowledge, the untiring efforts, and the insistence on maintaining the high standards of purity that are characteristic of scientists like Dr. Donald K. Tressler.

Chapter 4

•

HE PLANS FOR TOMORROW

MEET James F. Young, general manager of the General Electric Company's Atomic Products Division, whose office is in the plant at Palo Alto, California. He is a strikingly handsome fellow—six foot three, two hundred pounds, a high forehead and no gray visible in his wavy hair. Anyone who thinks an engineer is a quiet, shy daydreamer with a single-track mind should meet James Young.

An engineer by inclination and training, this remarkable man is a combination scientist, inventor, designer, educator and administrator. His business creed is expressed on the wall of his office by a Renouf painting titled "The Helping Hand." It shows a gnarled, kindly fisherman and a small girl seated in a rowboat. Mr. Young brought it with him from his Schenectady office to Palo Alto because it "fits beautifully" with his philosophy of management. He believes that a manager works for the people who report to him, a view that is contrary to actual practice in many companies.

Because he thinks first of human values, Dr. Young's influence has helped raise the living standards of many Americans. In an era when advancing technology usually is thought of in terms of space conquest or weapons of defense, he looks ahead to the translation of scientific progress into the fulfillment of human needs. One of General Electric's outstanding young engineers, this unusual man gives promise of someday becoming one of America's foremost scientists.

James F. Young was born in Philadelphia on January 4, 1917. Within eight months he was orphaned by the deadly flu epidemic, which took both of his parents. His godparents, Dr. Duncan Spaeth of Princeton University, the beloved English professor and rowing coach, and Mrs. Spaeth temporarily cared for the infant, and through their church in Princeton, New Jersey, arranged for the baby's adoption by Florence May and William Edwin Young, who had no children of their own. "Dad" Young, who had been a great athlete, fullback and pitcher, worked for the postal service. "Mother" Young, appreciative of having a son all "hers," gave Jim the same love and affection he could have expected from his own mother.

The Youngs lived in Wilsonborough, on the outskirts of Easton, Pennsylvania. Here Jim proved a good student, skipping second grade and taking top honors in his seventh grade class. The next year his marks fell, probably because his father withdrew the financial bonus for good grades, due to hard times.

A Life Scout, with 28 merit badges, Jim missed the remaining two required of an Eagle Scout because Red Cross and Swimming were then difficult to attain in his community. From an early age he was active in scouting and his "gang" controlled the membership of the troop almost like a club. To raise money the troop sold Fourth of July fireworks every year—an early form of Junior Achievement. The Scouts were good businessmen, enjoyed substantial credit, and Jim recalled that the fireworks they were able to buy on credit were valued as high as $5,500—more than his father's home was worth! One of the most profitable sales stratagems Jim developed was to talk to the parents of the boy who came to buy at the fireworks stand. Meanwhile his partner, a shorter lad, would be busy loading the boy's paper bag with all the firecrackers, pinwheels, sky rockets and sparklers it would hold. This lucrative enterprise earned the boys a two-week trip to Scout camp annually.

Dad Young, in common with most government employees, did not earn a large salary, and young Jim was encouraged to help as best he could. He cut the neighbors' lawns, sold newspapers, magazines and strawberries, and did odd jobs in the neighborhood. In between work, play and study he bought an old Ford for $10, reworked the whole engine, installed new pistons which he found on a nearby farm, and soon had a new engine and a speedy car for his trouble.

In addition to these activities he played the clarinet and sax in the school band and orchestra, ran on the track team, managed the baseball team, and worked on the school paper. By the time he reached his senior year at high school he had regained his academic drive. But his youth and lack of challenge during the early high school years limited his standing to 33rd in a class of 99. He took the College Board examinations hoping to win a scholarship at Lafayette College in nearby Easton. Although he missed this goal he did well enough so that the college granted him a loan. Earlier, Mrs. Duncan Spaeth had sent his family $500 toward tuition and it was expected that this sum and some extra earnings would see him through his first two years. After that he planned to work for a year and save enough money so that he could complete his education.

Unfortunately, Mrs. Spaeth's gift went to an orthodontist instead of the school treasurer, but Jim did so well in college that at the end of the second year Lafayette converted the loan to a scholarship.

Summer work helped pay Jim's living expenses. One vacation during the depression, he cut weeds at 25 cents an hour. Another year he obtained a job with the Metropolitan Edison, the local power company, at 45 cents an hour, working with the line crews. Thanks to the usual number of summer lightning storms and flash floods, he worked considerable overtime and averaged $40 a week, good pay for an eighteen-year-old boy in the mid-1930's.

Throughout the year he also played his sax and clarinet in a jazz band four nights a week.

"This earned me four or five dollars a night, plus a meal," he said, "and that meal was most important!"

Regardless of how late he was out on a job Saturday, sometimes to three or four in the morning, his mother insisted that he must be up to play in the Sunday school orchestra at nine o'clock the next day.

It was during his third summer at college that some of the engineering skill which later was to gain him national recognition began to show itself. Jim worked in Lancaster, Pennsylvania, for the Hamilton Watch Company which had a program of hiring college juniors. Here he developed a swedging process for making watch dials which the company adopted in its production line. This is a die-forming process that uses heavy Kraft paper and a brass punch press. Years later, as a going-away gift from his associates in General Electric's Household Refrigeration Department at Erie, Pennsylvania, Jim received a Hamilton watch with a dial of the type he had worked on as a college junior.

While at college Jim's original plan was to become a Navy pilot. He thought he would have a better chance to do this if he equipped himself with mechanical engineering as well as mathematics.

One of the administrators was Professor Ernest Fernald, with whom Jim discussed his thesis plan for honors.

"I've been thinking of doing an engineering study on the air conditioning of automobiles," Jim told him.

"Ridiculous!" exclaimed the professor. "That's a very impractical idea." Back in 1936 no one but a dreamer would have considered placing the then large, cumbersome air-conditioning system in a small car of that day. However, Professor Fernald finally did consent to Jim's doing a thesis on air conditioning of buses. On the day before Jim's oral examination, the Greyhound Corporation announced the first successful demonstration of bus air conditioning in Atlanta. Greyhound had used the same distribution system and the same refrigerant and compressor size as Jim had worked out for his Lafayette thesis.

"I had no trouble getting *that* thesis approved," he commented.

Although he did not belong to a fraternity at Lafayette (he lived at home), his campus leadership in various athletics earned him privileges at two of the Greek-letter houses, Phi Delta Theta and Sigma Chi. He played on their athletic teams and "loaned them my average." The average was good enough to earn him election to Phi Beta Kappa and Tau Beta Pi before he graduated *magna cum laude*, receiving his B.S. in mechanical engineering.

Two of Jim's professors did much to shape his eventual career with General Electric. One was Professor Paul B.

Eaton, head of Lafayette's Mechanical Engineering Department, whom Mr. Young describes as a "real teacher, an independent thinker who encouraged independent thought." Thanks to the influence of this man, Mr. Young later refused to consider conventional design patterns and constantly sought to dream up something new.

The other influence was Professor Lawrence Conover (still a consultant for General Electric, in addition to his college duties). At graduation Mr. Young had assurances of a fellowship at Yale, but if he were to take advantage of it he knew he would have to obtain some money to finance his living expenses. He decided to discuss the matter with Professor Conover.

"You see I have no way of raising any extra cash," Mr. Young explained. "I don't see how I can accept the fellowship."

"Why don't you take advantage of General Electric's advanced engineering training instead?" the other man asked. "They'll pay you while you learn."

The idea appealed to Mr. Young and he made an appointment to see the General Electric interviewer who was then on campus.

"A twenty-five-minute travesty," was the way Mr. Young described his interview with the General Electric recruiter, Charles Klein. Mr. Klein spent the entire time talking about General Electric's well-known test course but Mr. Young refused to comment or show any interest. Instead he kept asking about the company's famous advanced engineering course and Mr. Klein artfully dodged his questions. At the conclusion of the interview Mr. Young left discouraged.

He also received, among others, a promise of a job with duPont which he had decided to accept if General Electric did not make an offer. After he left Mr. Klein he was certain that there would be no opportunity to join General Electric.

"I'm inclined to call up that fellow and take the job with duPont," he told his dad.

"Why don't you sleep on it, Jim?" his father wisely suggested.

To his great surprise, next morning Mr. Young learned that Mr. Klein had left him a job offer before leaving the campus. He accepted it immediately.

Landing a position with General Electric—a company that was to project him into engineering prominence—was just the beginning. There still remained the problem of financing his move to the plant at Erie, Pennsylvania. Mr. Young solved it by staying on at Lafayette for two weeks after graduation and proctoring the annual forum for pre-college students. As soon as he had received his $40 fee he bought a new suit and a ticket to Erie, then took the first train out.

The history of General Electric dates back to 1878 when Thomas A. Edison founded the Edison Electric Light Company. In 1892 that company's successor merged with the Thomson Houston Electric Company to form the General Electric Company. The new concern grew rapidly to be the largest and one of the most diversified manufacturers of electrical equipment, apparatus and appliances of all types. In 1963 it had some 80 separate product departments, approximately 250,000 employees and 175 manufacturing units in 136 cities throughout the United States, Canada and Puerto Rico, all making and selling hundreds of different products.

It was only a short time before Mr. Young was transferred to Schenectady to join the advanced engineering course he had explored with Mr. Klein. There he became part of a group of bachelors who were taking General Electric's "A" class, plus the "B" and "C" classes. They lived at the Schenectady YMCA which had a one-year residency limit, but because these young engineers had helped the Y weather the 1938 recession, the manager let them stay on. Thus the stately brick edifice with its white columns that stood down on State Street near the Mohawk River bridge became sort of a fraternity for Mr. Young and his associates for four years.

This was an unusual group of would-be scientists. There was, for instance, John Robert Moore, later to become vice-president of North American Aviation and head of its Autonetics Division; Charlie Elston, who became general manager of General Electric's Large Steam Turbine-Generator Department in Schenectady, the largest operation of its kind in the world; Marvin Sledd, who later turned to the academic life and eventually headed the electrical engineering departments of Emery and Henry College and other schools. Seated just behind Mr. Young in the course office was Dr. Si Ramo, later a founding partner of the well-known Thompson Ramo Wooldridge organization, and others like Dr. Richard W. Porter of rocket and space fame.

Mr. Young did so well in these courses that in 1939 at the age of twenty-two he was made supervisor of General Electric's Mechanical Design Program, a newly established educational course which placed especial emphasis on invention. Two years later he advanced to take over administration of the Creative Engineering, Mechanical Engineering Training, and Analytical Consulting programs.

While he was enrolled in the original General Electric course called Mechanical Design, which was aimed at improving a young engineer's facility in the art of design, he objected strenuously to the way the course was taught. He felt that it did not accomplish what it could and that it was not a challenge to graduate engineers.

His protests did some good. It often happens that those who criticize a fault are invited to remedy it themselves. This was the result in this case; the company gave Mr. Young the job of running the course. He immediately changed the objectives and reshaped the perspectives. To reflect these changes it was renamed the Creative Engineering Course, most likely the first of its kind anywhere. Among the new ingredients, he introduced what today is known as "brainstorming." Mr. Osborn, the "O" of the famous Batten, Barton, Durstine and Osborn advertising agency, who traveled widely in behalf of creativity and brainstorming, worked with Mr. Young in redesigning the course, that being one of Osborn's early projects of this nature.

One added plus to the job for Mr. Young was the pretty secretary assigned to work with him. She was Rita Marie Shahan, a native of Schenectady.

"Rita and I had separate romances which died about the same time," Mr. Young recalled later. "A new one was born in the office and has blossomed ever since."

They were married on July 16, 1941, and later adopted two children, Sharon Margaret and James William, both of whom are left-handed.

From the time Mr. Young's first article, "The Nature of Pure Metals," appeared in *Mechanical Engineering* in 1943, leading trade magazines and professional societies have published his works. He found writing an enjoyable avocation and soon was working on his first book, *Materials and Processes*, written for the designer who would use materials and processes, rather than for the company which supplied them. This was a real *first* because such books are normally written by the suppliers or by chemists and metallurgists. The book had a profound influence on many universities and other companies which were impressed by General Electric's willingness to publish and share this kind of information usually kept a company secret.

In 1944 Mr. Young was transferred to the Appliance and Merchandise Department at Bridgeport, Connecticut, which, in common with most of the company, was heavily involved in war production.

"I did my first work here," Mr. Young commented. "I was responsible for devising engineering improvements to such strategic weapons as rocket launchers and torpedo gyroscopes. When the end of the war brought a booming market for new appliances I was put in charge of advance appliance engineering."

Mr. Young's personal philosophy and traits, combined with his alertness and energy, had much to do with his subsequent brilliant rise in the company.

"I'm one of those people who don't read deeply," Mr. Young said. "I read a great deal 'on the surface' but I cover lots of things. I watch closely, I listen a great deal, I learn every day. I try to add as much common sense as I can."

This statement reflects his allegiance to the motto of the Marquis de Lafayette, which he keeps framed in his office. It reads:

> I read, I study, I examine, I listen, I reflect—and out of all this I try to form an idea into which I put as much common sense as I can.—MARQUIS DE LAFAYETTE, 1777.

As manager of advance appliance engineering Mr. Young not only had to form ideas but to do so in relation to the future, for his group was responsible for developing appliances at least two to three years ahead of the time they would be placed on the market. In addition to working on future plans, he was responsible for selecting and training new engineers for his staff as well as consulting on technical matters with other scientists elsewhere in the company. A national advertisement featured him as one of General Electric's outstanding engineers. "He Plans for Tomorrow —The Story of Jim Young" was the title of the ad which contained sketches of Jim as a boy, on the job, and at home with his wife, Rita.

"Many of the ideas we worked on at that time are still coming into the market," Mr. Young remarked in 1963.

In 1949 he was assigned to the Household Refrigerator Department to work on refrigerating machines. This job was a natural for a man whose interest in refrigeration started back during his college days, and he worked enthusiastically on the design of refrigeration units, home food freezers, room air conditioners and room dehumidifiers. It was his ingenuity which was responsible for countless innovations and improvements in these products, some of which are described and covered in the 20 patents issued in Mr. Young's name.

It was only natural that Mr. Young should come to the attention of Clarence H. Linder, then vice-president, Engineering Services, who asked that this young engineer be appointed as consultant on engineering studies and surveys, a post which gave Mr. Young opportunity to bring his experience and wisdom to a multitude of problems, many of which were in the formative stage. Here he was given the broad responsibility for teaching, consulting, and appraising technical work throughout many branches of the company.

It was while he was still affiliated with Engineering Services that he began to become interested in the challenging field of energy conversion. He began to investigate unconventional combinations of energy sources and electrical energy conversion processes and contributed much new knowledge to this increasingly important subject. It was logical, therefore, that he should be appointed manager of the General Engineering Laboratory in 1958. It was some 60 years earlier that Steinmetz had first performed many engineering feats in this famous developmental laboratory, and it was in these facilities that the beloved Dr. Irving Langmuir spent much of his time.

In his new post Mr. Young guided developmental work on fuel cells, equipment which converts the chemical energy of a fuel directly into electrical energy. The practical success of that effort was later demonstrated in 1962 when General Electric was awarded a contract to build a fuel cell power system for the Gemini space vehicle. Other significant developments that were initiated or progressed under his management in the laboratory were water purification processes, cryogenics, thermoplastic recording, air pollution, solid state power conversion and thin-film electronics.

Cryogenics, the study of the behavior of metals at temperatures near absolute zero, became one of Young's newest interests. A practical application of the research conducted under his direction was the development of a cryogenic gyroscope with which he hoped to achieve a superaccurate inertial guidance system for missiles. The cover of *Mechanical Engineering* for March, 1960, featured a sketch of Mr. Young and an associate studying a gyroscope in their laboratory.

In 1960 Mr. Young became general manager of the

Electric Utility Engineering Operation. Three years later he was advanced to the post of general manager of the company's atomic products division.

In each of his administrative positions Mr. Young was an inspiring leader because he firmly believed that a manager worked for the people reporting to him. He has aided technological advance not only by his personal achievements but also through his able direction of his associates' work. His understanding of widely diverse technical problems, his power of keen analysis, and above all, the flow of ideas from a creative mind were invaluable contributions to the success of all the activities he directed.

Away from the job Mr. Young does not lack for things to do. He is especially fond of family sports as a spectator and participant. He still enjoys stamp collecting, photography, boating, and woodworking when there is time for these hobbies. Apart from his primary interests in his home, family and job, perhaps Mr. Young's single greatest concern is to do all he can to insure the highest standards of integrity for the professional man. He believes firmly that the professional man must maintain his personal independence, see his responsibility as one of giving unselfish service to others, and not permit himself to be dominated or dictated to by management, labor, political parties or other groups. Through innumerable lectures and printed papers he has urged a clearer understanding of this unique responsibility which he believes falls on the scientist and engineer.

To young people who wonder whether they should pursue a scientific career, he has this to say:

"A scientist must be an educated man first and a scientist second. He must have the humanistic, cultural, social and economic background (in knowledge)—both historic and contemporary. With this background in mind he must then evaluate his own possibilities of making a contribution to scientific knowledge and engineering applications."

An engineer does not have to look forward to a lifetime career at a drafting board. If he has imagination, reads widely, dares to be an independent thinker, looks to the future, knows how to organize his own work and that of others and has leadership qualities, there is no limit to where he may go.

Jim Young is proof of this.

Chapter 5

•

"I AM THE CEMENT"

"RESPECTED friend:—" was the unusual and heart-warming Quaker salutation on the letter I received from Dr. Lippert. "I want to warn you," he wrote, "that I am still skeptical that I can provide the proper subject for your book, but I will be happy to explore it when you visit us." And then the friendly closing: "Respectfully your friends, Joseph Bancroft & Sons Co., Arnold L. Lippert."

I was positive that Dr. Lippert would prove the perfect textile scientist.

Two weeks later I traveled to Wilmington and taxied out to the modern yellow brick research building perched near the edge of a bluff overlooking the swift Brandywine River far below. A pleasant receptionist took my hat and coat.

"Upstairs and past the research library to the end of the corridor," she directed me. I found Dr. Lippert in his large, inviting office about to take a long-distance call. There was a warm smile as he waved me in and motioned to a chair by his desk. It was evident from the phone conversation that this soft-spoken bespectacled man not only took a genuine interest in the personal welfare of his men but that he was also an able administrator who could and did make decisions when needed.

"I thought you were looking for a working scientist," he

66

said after we had chatted briefly. "Are you certain that you want to include me? I'm only the cement in this operation."

"That may be, but I'm told you're one of the outstanding scientists in your field," I replied, "and I feel confident that your story is worth telling!"

As he gradually told me about himself I knew that I had been correct.

Arnold L. Lippert was born November 12, 1910, in Kewanee, Illinois, the son of Nellie B. James and Helmuth A. Lippert, a skilled stonecutter.

Although a hard-working and excellent student, Arnold found time to become so proficient on the clarinet that when he entered high school he was invited to join the band. In addition he was active as a debater, serving as captain of two championship teams. As graduation neared, he was undecided whether to become a chemist or a lawyer. He liked his chemistry courses and thought that he would enjoy a scientific career but because he was so fond of debating he also wanted to study for the law. Finally he decided in favor of chemistry because he realized that he could not afford three years of law school after college plus the necessary incubation period required of most young attorneys.

Arnold knew that if he hoped to attend college he would have to pay most of his own expenses, for his father was unable to help much. To that end he took every job that came along, whether it was clerking in a store, lugging water for a road construction crew, playing his clarinet in a band concert, or doing odd jobs in the neighborhood. For some time he was the representative in his area for the Curtis Publishing Company, selling subscriptions for their magazines.

Although he received several offers of scholarships to other colleges, Arnold chose the University of Illinois because of its reputation for being the country's top chemistry school and because tuition was less expensive for residents of the state. Here he majored in chemistry and spent much of his spare time in dramatics and playing his clarinet for school events. Summers he earned money working at clerical and laboring jobs as well as playing in various bands.

Following graduation with a B.S. and high honors, including Phi Beta Kappa, in 1931, Mr. Lippert was anxious to continue his scientific training at Johns Hopkins and fortunately was the Illinois winner of a scientific fellowship that paid $1,000 a year for postgraduate study. This sum was enough to cover all his expenses, and for the first time in many years he was relieved of financial worries. Mr. Lippert had been a faithful church attendant all his life but at the Mt. Vernon Methodist Church in Baltimore he found an added reason for regularity. It was attractive Lela Bichell whom he first met there at Sunday service. Soon he was not only sitting next to her at church but calling frequently at her home.

Except for odd jobs, he was unable to find any regular summer employment because the depression had set in. However, one July he worked for a few weeks at duPont's rayon plant in Buffalo, New York. This gave him some practical experience as well as an entrée into the duPont organization. Accordingly when he received his Ph.D. in June of 1934, he interviewed for several jobs and decided to accept a position with duPont as a research chemist at the Experimental Station in Wilmington, Delaware. He remained there only four months, however, because his services were sought by the nearby textile firm of Joseph Bancroft & Sons Company which needed a man with an extensive technical background. In December of 1934, Dr. Lippert reported to this old established firm, located two miles above the center of Wilmington on the Brandywine River, to become technical assistant to the general superintendent.

Joseph Bancroft was born in England in 1803 and as a young man served a seven-year apprenticeship in an English textile mill. Meanwhile, his family had immigrated to the United States and opened a flannel mill in Wilmington, Delaware. When Joseph finished his apprenticeship in 1824 he joined his family and immediately took over the management of his father's factory. Periodic lack of water at that site forced the family to move their business elsewhere but Joseph remained behind and was hired by William Young to manage his mill at Rockford some two miles up the Brandywine River from the village of Wilmington. Both off and on the job young Bancroft learned as much about the business as possible, and with borrowed capital acquired from William Young a 2½-story mill building, a 2-story boiler house (used for heating in winter), a large stone dwelling house, a stone barn and three smaller buildings. With a few hand-picked employees and determination to produce the very best cloths that could be made, he began the manufacture of cotton cloth on March 25, 1831.

Joseph Bancroft brought not only technical know-how to the business but, perhaps just as important, certain firm convictions and ideas about the kind of relationships he would have with his employees. Because he was a Quaker, all of his business dealings were conducted in accordance with the beliefs and principles of the Friends.

First of all he insisted that his workers be well housed. To achieve this he converted the large stone barn into four dwellings and built other homes as soon as possible, allowing ample ground so each worker might have a garden. Then, on the very first Friday night after production had started, he called his employees together and gave them their week's pay in cash. He chose Friday because locally Saturday was the shopping day. Furthermore, he hated the economic conditions that often resulted when workers were forced to buy at company stores, and he insisted that his employees should be free to shop wherever they pleased. Since that time until December of 1962 (when all wages were paid by check), through depressions, business reverses and panics, the Friday pay in cash for all employees except executives never failed at the Bancroft plants although Joseph and his successors often had to make heroic efforts to meet the payroll.

The business gradually grew and prospered, and by the end of 1865 Joseph Bancroft was at last out of debt. About that same time he admitted his two sons, William and Samuel, into a co-partnership known as Joseph Bancroft & Sons. With William running the cotton factory and Samuel supervising the finishing operation as well as developing new lines of work, the father could take things easier. As he grew older he devoted more and more time to trying to heal the breach between the Orthodox and Hicksite branches of the Society of Friends. On one of his many trips speaking to Friends on the cause of unity he contracted pneumonia and died on December 7, 1874.

Under the direction of the two Bancroft sons the business continued to expand and maintain its position of leadership in the industry. One of the company's many triumphs was its development of Sun-Fast Holland shades: "the only Holland in the world that will not fade by exposure to the sun." Thanks to this innovation Bancroft soon dominated the shade-cloth market. Among its other pioneering endeavors, it was the first firm in this country to do mercerizing for the trade. (Mercerizing is the process of treating cotton thread or cloth with a caustic alkali solution to strengthen it, give it a silky luster and make it more receptive to dyes.)

Bancroft book cloths achieved such a fine reputation that in 1908 its "Legal Buckram" was selected as standard binding for all books filed for record by the Bureau of Standards, the Librarian of Congress, the Public Printer and the American Library Association. Thereafter the demand for Hollands and book cloths became so great that the company could not keep up with the orders that poured into the factory every day.

In 1916 the company produced some of the first rayon made in America and developed a process for finishing cotton fabrics in which the individual cotton fibers were encased in a sheath of rayon, thus producing a firm cloth that withstood countless washings. This so-called "Basco" finish proved an immediate success and millions of units of "Basco" treated damask were sold.

In addition to constantly adding new buildings and facilities on the property that stretched along the Brandywine River, the company purchased the Reading Cotton Mills in Reading, Pennsylvania, in 1910. In 1925 it acquired the business founded by William Simpson in 1836 which specialized in the printing of silks, calicoes and other cloths. It was located in Chester, Pennsylvania, and became known as the Print Works Division of the Bancroft Company.

In the 1930's when textiles suffered along with all business from the effects of the depression, the Bancroft management realized that it must introduce something new in order to strengthen the company's financial position. But what should it be?

As the first step, in 1936 Dr. Lippert was appointed a member of the company's Operations Committee and also made chemical director of the three plants. Thus the Research Department was born, with Dr. Lippert, aided by two technical assistants and a secretary, its director. From this date on more and more emphasis was to be placed on research that would lead to the development of new products.

William R. MacIntyre, then vice-president of Bancroft, already had been searching for a method of making a better chintz. Up to that time there had been no genuinely durable chintz because the crispness of this material was obtained by using starches or gums in the finish but these disappeared entirely after a few washings. A number of trial runs had been made using various kinds of coating materials, even rayon, but none proved satisfactory.

"Why don't you explore this problem?" Mr. MacIntyre asked his young research director one day. "You have the scientific knowledge that might just come up with the answer."

Dr. Lippert immediately went to work and by eliminating all the chemical formulas and processes which he knew would not do the job, was able to start out fresh with some ideas of his own. It was not long before he worked out a different chemical formula which produced a new type of chintz, that "retains the luster even after repeated laundering, is spot proof, appreciably fire resistant, flexible and foldable."

Everyone at Bancroft was amazed and delighted, and the impact of the new "Everglaze" chintz on the market was startling. Other textile printers and finishers asked if they might have a license to make chintz using the "Everglaze" process and late in 1939 a limited licensing program was instituted. As the number of licenses grew, with a corresponding increase in royalties, the management realized that Dr. Lippert's invention could change the company's entire future. From this time on, Joseph Bancroft & Sons ceased to be just another bleaching, dyeing, printing and finishing firm, but became one of the leaders in the textile field as it devoted more of its energies and money to research and development and expanded its licensing activities.

Perhaps of even more interest was the change which this made in Dr. Lippert's career. A highly trained scientist whose knowledge of chemical engineering seemingly made him most valuable in the research laboratory, he gradually found himself more concerned with business matters than with research. As companies were licensed to use the patented "Everglaze" finish Dr. Lippert was confronted with numerous problems for which his training at Illinois and Johns Hopkins left him totally unprepared.

It was necessary to work out financial arrangements with each licensee, which called for the skill of a salesman and an accountant. Contracts, which had to be drawn up, negotiated and finally agreed upon, required the brains of a lawyer. Each licensing company had to be shown how to set up its machinery in order to adapt it to the process, necessitating the knowledge of a master mechanic. And finally, the licensees had to be shown how to market their new "Everglaze" product successfully, demanding the services of an expert in advertising and promotion. Although Dr. Lippert did not pretend to know all of these fields he was, nevertheless, responsible for seeing that the over-all licensing program was carried out, and in a short time he became not only a research director but a general manager as well.

"I am merely the cement that held those various functions together," Dr. Lippert insisted with characteristic modesty.

Despite all of the work connected with the licensing program, Dr. Lippert also kept the research activities humming along at top speed. Further fruits of this endeavor were realized in 1940 when the company introduced its "Staze-Rite" washable marquisette and organdy fabrics together with its "Ban-Dri" permanent water-repellent fabrics.

In November of 1941, as the nation quietly prepared to meet the threat of a full-scale war, the government sought out the most able men in each industry to serve in the Office of Production Management. It was no surprise to Dr. Lippert's superiors when his services were requested and he was thereupon appointed chief of the Dyeing and Finishing Branch of the Office of Production Management. A month later the country was at war and Dr. Lippert soon became a dollar-a-year man, serving in a dual capacity as chief of the Dyeing and Finishing Branch of the War Production Board and chief of the Dyestuff Section as well as on the top administrative level as chairman of the Dyestuffs Advisory Committee. For the next three years he was responsible for administering all technical matters connected with the Textile Section which controlled the production and allocation of all textile plants in the country and all uses made of dyes.

These were busy days for Dr. Lippert. He had married Miss Bichell in 1936, and by this time his family included two small daughters who saw little of their father. He was working six days a week in Washington and spending the seventh back at Bancroft where research was now concentrated on adapting existing processes and developing new ones to meet the countless urgent needs of the armed forces.

Bancroft processed over 425,000,000 yards of fabrics for essential war purposes. The company finished materials ranging from balloon cloth to burlap, from book cloths for binding textbooks and manuals to cartridge cloth for powder bags, from maps to mildewproof clothing and accessories, from tents to twill fatigue suits, from signal flags to seersucker for Nurses, Wacs, Waves, Spars and Women Marines, as well as countless articles of clothing for male and female members of the armed forces.

In November of 1944, Dr. Lippert was relieved of his Washington responsibilities and returned to Bancroft, his research department now numbering some fifteen technicians and clerical assistants. The following year war secrecy was lifted from "Ban-Flame," a revolutionary flame-retardant and mildewproof finish, suitable for all types of fibrous fabrics. Once other textile companies learned that this invention did not change the appearance or texture of cloths, there was an immediate demand for the product.

At the end of World War II, Dr. Lippert and his staff prepared to give a vigorous push to their "Everglaze" program once again. In this connection Bancroft was one of the original scholarship sponsors of "The Miss America Pageant Scholarship Fund." Miss America was to be chosen annually on the basis of her talent, appearance in evening dress, and over-all personality. (This competition had nothing to do with the former beauty contests also held at Atlantic City.) The winner received a valuable scholarship to continue her education, plus a year's contract to make personal appearances, part of her time being allocated to Bancroft. Miss Bess Myerson was the first winner and she and her successors appeared at style shows and promotions both here and abroad helping promote the "Everglaze" fabrics.

The success of the "Everglaze" program encouraged the management to look to Dr. Lippert's research group for new ideas and products that would add to the company's profitable operation. From time to time Dr. Lippert added new researchers to the staff, choosing his men carefully with the aim of forming a well-rounded organization whose members would work together closely and cooperate with each other. Because resins are basic to so much of the research conducted in a textile laboratory, Dr. Lippert made arrangements to combine Bancroft's research on the mechanical use of resins with investigations being conducted by two foreign organizations, the Calico Printers of Great Britain and Raduner of Switzerland. As a result of this cooperative effort Dr. Lippert added some European technicians to his staff, giving it more depth.

Another important licensing program developed and promoted under Dr. Lippert's direction carried the trademark "Ban-Lon," a process which had its beginnings about 1947 in the research laboratory of Alexander Smith, Inc., a rug manufacturer (now Mohasco Industries, Inc.). At that time the price of clean wool from India was 43 cents a pound whereas clean wool from South America cost but 18 cents a pound. The Indian wool, when used in carpet making, covered well and had a rich, live appearance, but the South American wool was skimpy in cover, had a dull, flat look, and did not spin well. The great difference in price would make the South American wool attractive, however, if it could ever be made usable.

The Alexander Smith researchers developed and patented a crimping process which made the South American wool serviceable, but for a number of reasons the company was unable to get into production. In 1953 representatives of Alexander Smith asked the Bancroft management if it would be interested in marketing these patents. This promised to be another licensing and promotion program similar to the successful "Everglaze" project—but with one exception. Whereas "Everglaze" had developed along with Bancroft's normal finishing business, the crimping process was in the field of fibers, filaments, yarns, and knitting operations with which Bancroft personnel were not familiar. Furthermore, much work would have to be done to perfect and develop the original patents before they could be marketed to rug manufacturers.

When they broached the subject to him, top management wanted to know what Dr. Lippert thought of the idea. With his usual calm assurance he replied that there was no question but what his men could tackle the problem and lick it. That settled the matter, and after Dr. Lippert had hired a number of new employees from Alexander Smith who were familiar with the process, he had it patented as "Ban-Lon" and registered this trademark in the United States and 50 principal foreign countries. Like "Everglaze," the "Ban-Lon" was an immediate success, amply justifying the faith that Dr. Lippert had expressed in his scientists.

During the years following World War II, in addition to his duties at Joseph Bancroft & Sons, Dr. Lippert served on numerous advisory committees operating under the National Academy of Science. Perhaps the most important was the Committee on Flame and Thermal Combat Protective Clothing which was responsible for planning adequate protection for soldiers exposed to nuclear warfare.

Between 1956 and 1957 some 33 textile finishing plants throughout the country failed. Many of them suffered from overproduction, had been overstocked at the end of the

Korean War, or were unable to make a profit because of mounting labor costs. Due to its diversification program which was responsible for its profitable "Everglaze" and "Ban-Lon" licensing programs, the Bancroft Mills did not share the industry's woes although in 1955 it had been forced to close its Reading plant because it was no longer operating profitably.

As Dr. Lippert's engineering and research staffs continued to grow, office and laboratory space became increasingly crowded. Finally, he realized his long-standing dream—a brand-new research building. Known as Research Laboratory No. 2, the two-story and basement building was constructed and occupied in 1960 to provide offices for Dr. Lippert and his staff, the entire engineering group, as well as laboratory facilities for special chemical research projects.

By 1963 some 300 employees were working in the department which now consisted of three sections: chemical research, developmental engineering, and marketing. By this time Joseph Bancroft & Sons had become a subsidiary of Indian Head Mills and Dr. Lippert had advanced to the post of senior executive vice-president of the company. In addition to a busy schedule at Wilmington, his responsibilities required him to do extensive traveling abroad, visiting the many company offices located in numerous foreign countries throughout the world.

Such activity does not leave Dr. Lippert much time for home or family but he makes the most of every minute wherever he may be.

"I haven't played the clarinet for some time," he said, "but I usually find time to swim in my pool and do about a quarter of a mile in the evening." In the winter he shifts to the local Y pool, for he feels that swimming gives him the best exercise he can get.

A strong believer that every man should pull his weight in his profession, community and church, Dr. Lippert has long been active in the American Chemical Society and has served the Delaware Research Foundation. When his daughters were attending high school he served in his local district as chairman of the Citizens Advisory Committee and later exchanged this work to serve as a trustee of the local Presbyterian church. The young grandfather of his oldest daughter Norma's two children, Dr. Lippert enjoys having his other girls home occasionally. Lynn, a senior at Cornell, chose to follow in her father's footsteps as a chemistry major, and Arlene, like Norma, studied at Duke to become a registered nurse.

Dr. Lippert is another example of a scientist who climbed to the top echelon of a company to become, as he expresses it, the "cement" or the over-all manager. Most students who look forward to a scientific career usually think of their future in terms of working in a laboratory or directing engineering or other research projects. This is not necessarily true today because, as in Dr. Lippert's case, industry is turning more and more to the scientist for help in directing the over-all business operation. Thus a new dimension has been added to the scientist's profession.

Chapter 6

•

RUBBER WAS HIS BUSINESS

SUNDAY morning was unusually peaceful at Police Headquarters in downtown Seattle, Washington. The officer on duty was catching up on some reports when the phone rang.

"Police Headquarters. Sergeant Brown speaking."

"The whole town's blowing up!" an excited woman was shrieking. "Come quickly!"

Then over the phone there came the sound of a muffled boom.

The sergeant turned white. "Where are you? What's your address?"

"Twenty-fifth Avenue, N. E., just north of the university."

The police officer hung up the phone and reached for another instrument. In 1922 there was no two-way radio and he had to call the police station nearest the University of Washington.

"There's some terrible explosions up near the university," he roared into the receiver. "Send all available men."

Five minutes later with sirens blowing, a police emergency truck turned up Twenty-fifth Avenue, N. E., and the driver peered anxiously, seeking the trouble. All was quiet except for a handful of people standing near an empty lot.

"Where's the explosion?" a burly policeman yelled, and jumped from the automobile even before it had stopped.

A man pointed toward the woods at the end of the street. "In there—some nut from the college is trying to blow us up."

The police raced into the woods in this isolated section of the university campus and found two young men tamping a white powder into a small copper tube.

"What's going on here?" demanded the officer in charge. "What's the idea disturbing the neighborhood—and on a Sunday morning at that?"

The taller of the two men jumped to his feet. "Sorry, officer, we didn't mean to make so much noise. We're just testing an idea for new blasting caps."

"Blasting caps! And on Sunday morning . . . who are you, anyway?"

"Waldo L. Semon. I'm a teaching assistant here at the university." His six-foot-two height and sturdy physique towered over the short, thin policeman. "My friend here is a chemist. We were just trying to find out how this new detonator works with various types of dynamite."

"And on Sunday morning?" the officer interrupted. "I ought to lock you both up for disturbing the peace. Now get back to your classroom and don't let me catch you here again."

The incident was typical of Semon's desire to satisfy his curiosity as he experimented with new ideas. A man who has always enjoyed work and keeping busy, he spent his working days constantly thinking up new ideas, trying them out and learning.

Waldo Semon was born September 10, 1898, at Demopolis, Alabama, where his father was working as a civil engineer supervising the construction of the town's light and power plant. Later he built a similar plant at Hattiesburg, Mississippi, and then an ice plant at Demopolis. Even today, although the family left Demopolis before he was quite two years old, Dr. Semon can still recall the eerie sound of the ice plant's siren and the sight of wagons loaded with cotton bales rumbling through the muddy streets.

Until Waldo turned seven his family was constantly on the move. Allegan, Michigan; Gallipolis and Pomeroy, Ohio; Philadelphia, Pennsylvania; Washington, D. C., and numerous other places were some of their homes until they finally settled in Seattle, Washington, where Mr. Semon took a position in the city's engineering office. It was not until Waldo completed sixth grade that they moved again, this time to Medford, Oregon, where he finished grade school and began his secondary education. But then it was Ashland, Oregon, next it was Eugene, Oregon, and finally the family went back to Seattle where Waldo finished his high school studies.

Even as a young boy Waldo had a tremendous capacity for work and used every minute to good advantage. During the summer vacations he picked hops, prunes, and strawberries on the lush farmlands of the Pacific Northwest. On one construction job he was water boy, on another he dug ditches for a dollar a day. When he was only fifteen he borrowed a horse and buggy and traveled 160 miles to a point northwest of Portland to join a surveying crew for the summer.

"Your job's to go ahead of the surveyors and cut out the brush and undergrowth so the men can get through," the boss told him, believing that the boy was much older than he actually was. Within a few weeks' time someone else was doing the hard work and Waldo was made first a chainman and then rodman. A couple of weeks later the boss called him into his makeshift office.

"Pete tells me you're quite a mathematician." He pushed his hat to one side and scratched his head as though he were not quite sure.

"I like math," Waldo replied, "and it's one of my best subjects at school."

"How would you like to borrow my 'slip-stick' and get in a little extra practice?"

"That would be swell," the boy replied without hesitation, and he was soon figuring all of the crew's precise measurements with the help of a slide rule.

After graduating from high school he joined the state highway commission, feeling that he was too young to go on to college. He became rodman on the engineering crew that supervised the building of a highway through the thick forest and over the summit of the steep Cascade Mountains near Mount Rainier, Washington. That fall he barely got out of the mountains before a raging blizzard blew in and filled the roads and trails with such a deep blanket of snow that part of the construction crew was trapped in the mountains for some time.

In September, 1916, he entered the University of Washington, determined to become a chemist, thanks to an inspiring chemistry teacher under whom he had studied in high school. The teacher had lent him some old German chemistry textbooks and he found the material on organic chemistry "the most inspiring thing I had ever read."

It was no time before young Semon was marked by his professors as an unusual student, one who could grasp every problem and always work out the correct solution. Although chemistry was his chief interest, he nevertheless read widely in many other fields.

By the time his first summer vacation had begun, the country was at war. The U. S. Geological Survey needed men to help chart the coastline for defense purposes and Waldo eagerly joined the crew that went up the Olympic peninsula. When he returned to school that fall he was asked to devote his spare time to undertaking special work for the United States Intelligence Service analyzing various inks to be used for code messages. And as the Army hunted for a new gas for warfare, he made a selenium analogue of mustard gas for the government.

The following summer he joined a crew that was building a spur line of the Milwaukee Railroad through the Olympic peninsula. The new track would enable freight trains to bring out spruce logs badly needed for the manufacture of airplanes. For Waldo the job was short-lived because the draft board called him in July and back he went to the University of Washington to join the Students Army Training Corps. Always eager to fill in spare time, he volunteered to experiment on an improved synthesis for TNT and other explosives, but in November the war ended and he returned to regular student life.

The year 1920 was a memorable one. In June Waldo graduated *cum laude* and was showered with honors by the university. In the fall of that year he married a classmate, Marjorie Gunn, whom he had first met in chemistry class during freshman year. Like her husband, she had ended her college career with top honors.

The life of the young couple continued to center about chemistry. Mrs. Semon tutored would-be chemists while her husband taught at the university as an assistant in the chemistry department and also continued his studies during his spare time and at night. In 1923 he received his Ph.D. plus a promotion to the position of instructor.

Now that he had his advanced degree, Dr. Semon added to his income by serving as a consulting chemist to private industry in his spare time. In addition he wrote numerous articles which were published in various chemical and scientific journals. In 1926 one of these attracted the attention of a research chemist at the Eastman Kodak Company, who in turn mentioned the excellence of the treatise to Dr. Harlan L. Trumbull, director of rubber and textile research for the B. F. Goodrich Company in Akron, Ohio.

During the early years of Dr. Semon's college career, Dr. Trumbull had taught at the University of Washington where he had been in charge of the freshman chemical laboratory.

"Semon—of course—Waldo Semon," Dr. Trumbull said as he talked with the man at Eastman Kodak. "He was one of our most promising students. I remember him well."

As soon as Dr. Trumbull returned to Akron he sent a telegram to Dr. Semon offering him a position in the department of chemical research at B. F. Goodrich. A wire of acceptance was soon received and Dr. Semon was launched on his career in rubber research.

It was not long before Dr. Trumbull's faith in the young chemist was justified. He had suggested to Dr. Semon that his first assignment might be to survey a certain process that had been suggested for the production of a rubber which might be especially suitable for use as an adhesive. After three months of intensive research and probing for the right combination of molecules, the new employee came to Dr. Trumbull's office and asked, "I wonder if I might follow some ideas of my own for this study?"

"Of course, by all means," Dr. Trumbull replied. "We want you to feel free to follow your own inclinations whenever you wish."

As a result, Dr. Semon was responsible for the creation

of Koroseal, the extremely versatile vinyl that has proved superior in many ways to natural rubber. Even today this amazing material is still serving men and industry in many important ways, following a distinguished war record when practically the entire output of Koroseal was assigned to products used by the armed services.

After this achievement Dr. Semon created more than a score of new chemicals called age resistors because they give rubber a longer useful life and better resistance to the effects of heat, bending, and the atmosphere. In addition to this research, he turned his attention to some of the technical problems of bonding rubber to metal, and many of his ideas for making improved rubber articles and consumer products were patented.

As the threat of a world war grew during the late 1930's, the management of B. F. Goodrich reached an important decision which was to involve Dr. Semon. One day the research director called him into his office.

"No doubt you are aware that if there should be a war the United States might no longer be able to import crude rubber from the East Indies," he said.

Dr. Semon nodded. This possibility had been bothering him for some time because rubber is one of the most important raw materials for tires and thirty thousand other useful products.

"We want you to undertake intensive research and see if you can develop a material to replace rubber in the event of a national emergency," the director continued. "All of our research chemists, chemical engineers and compounders, as well as technicians in other divisions of the company, will be available to help you. We want you to plan and coordinate the whole job."

First some thousands of different types of synthetic rubber were prepared in the laboratory and evaluated. Then, on the basis of economic and engineering analysis, Dr. Semon chose one that could be made from materials that were relatively cheap and abundant. The new synthetic rubber, called Ameripol, was developed further on the test-tube scale. Next a small pilot factory was built to see what problems might arise when actual manufacturing in a larger plant started. Finally, the machinery and equipment which would be needed for full-scale production were developed, constructed and put into use. In 1940 a number of passenger car tires were made and tested in which natural rubber in the treads, sidewalls, and around the cords was replaced with Ameripol. After proving out by road tests they were sold on the open market—the first tires ever offered the American public that had been made with synthetic rubber. Actually they were so good many were still in use five years later.

In addition to this work on Ameripol, Dr. Semon and his group pioneered the manufacture of nitrile rubber in this country. This was a special rubber able to resist swelling and damage caused by oil. It was first produced by him on a pilot scale in 1938. Dr. Semon became vice-president and director of research of the Hycar Chemical Company which built the plant and manufactured the nitrile rubber called Hycar. Little wonder that in 1940 Dr. Semon was given national recognition and named a "modern pioneer" by an award committee headed by Dr. Karl T. Compton of Massachusetts Institute of Technology, who chose him as an outstanding contributor to industrial progress.

During World War II, Dr. Semon aided the government with the development and engineering design of many synthetic rubber plants. He resigned his post as vice-president of the Hycar Chemical Company to spend full time on research, which had always been of greatest interest to him. For his contributions to the development of butadiene synthetic rubber the American Chemical Society honored him with the Charles Goodyear Award in 1946.

Following the war, Dr. Semon became increasingly interested in research projects conducted in Europe. In 1954 he spent some time in Germany in the laboratory of Dr. Ziegler. From there he brought back to this country chemical ideas and methods for making strong and hard polyethylene, a process which has been developed and placed into extensive commercial production.

After explaining the principles he had learned while at Dr. Ziegler's laboratory, Dr. Semon urged his group of researchers and chemists to try to make new synthetic rubbers using Ziegler chemistry. Late one afternoon one of the men called excitedly: "Doctor Semon, Doctor Semon. Come here! I've got it!"

The famous chemist hurried across the room and peered over the man's shoulder at a small sticky lump and a telltale trace on an infrared chart.

"Wonderful! Without doubt you have synthesized the molecule of tree rubber!" And acting as proud as if he had made the discovery himself, Dr. Semon extended his hand. "Congratulations," he said. "Today you have accomplished what rubber chemists have been trying to do for a hundred years!"

Dr. Semon's associates report that he is always anxious to help others with their job. One young associate once asked the scientist's advice about a research problem and after following his suggestions found the material he was seeking.

"When I returned to report my success to Dr. Semon," he said, "I could see that it was no surprise to him. He had solved my problem at the very start and had merely pointed me in the right direction."

Both Dr. and Mrs. Semon are interested in Old English architecture and live in a Tudor-style country home, Brandywine Cottage, on the outskirts of Akron. Their three daughters are married to a chemist, a physicist and a civil engineer, respectively. Brandywine Cottage is a lively place when the eleven grandchildren swoop down on their grandparents for a visit.

Dr. Semon also has a farm where he relaxes and tries out some of his agricultural ideas. He finds hard work more restful than golf for keeping him physically fit and close to nature. With his interest in the outdoors he is well qualified to serve as he does year after year on the Akron Metropolitan Park Board.

Perhaps the secret of Dr. Semon's success in business has been the fact that he so thoroughly enjoys his work. He will spend hours in the library searching through chemical literature for facts which may serve as the basis of a new theory or lead to a new product for the company to manufacture. Nor does five o'clock necessarily mean the end of his working day. Since work is fun and he enjoys every minute of it, his friends often find him working far into the night on some new or interesting chemical project.

"Few scientists can count on working only eight-hour days," he says, "and if they are dedicated to their work, they don't even notice the time!"

•

Chapter 7

THE SCIENTIST TURNED
BUSINESSMAN

D URING the 1958 commencement ceremony at Rennselaer Polytechnic Institute, a tall slim man who had a
rather young face and a carefully trimmed mustache stood
up to receive his honorary Doctor of Science degree. In re-
ferring to his accomplishments, Dr. R. C. Folsom, president
of Rennselaer, said in part:

"One of his prime interests has been education and the
critical need for it in today's troubled world. . . . A vigorous
champion of the highest quality in education, he has urged
more productive effort in those basic intellectual and spirit-
ual disciplines that would increase the yield of truly en-
lightened people leading fruitful lives in a world of peace."

The man, Monroe E. Spaght, upon whom the degree was
conferred was not—as might be expected—an educator, but
a leading American scientist and a foremost industrialist
who was soon to become the chief executive of one of the
nation's largest petroleum enterprises, the Shell Oil Company.

Monroe E. Spaght (pronounced "Spate") was born on
December 9, 1909, out in the country near a small northern
California city called Eureka, the Greek word for "I have

found [it]," Archimedes' exclamation when in his bath, he thought of a way to determine the purity of gold by displacement of mass. Monroe was the son of Frederick E. and Alpha Light Spaght, whose ancestors had sailed in 1847 from New England around the Horn to California, where they settled and remained.

As a boy Monroe was a brilliant student, interested in chemistry and music, and showed considerable aptitude for the trombone which he sometimes played as a professional musician. In 1929, at the age of nineteen, he received an A.B. degree from Stanford University and then took an M.A. in chemistry there the following year.

But this education had not come easily in some respects. Times were hard, and the family resources were very limited. The first years of college were at the Humboldt State Teachers College in nearby Arcata, and he could live at home. Summer and weekend work on the farms and in the lumber mills helped greatly, and a small college orchestra supplied more of that shortest commodity—money.

During his first two years at Stanford the family made great sacrifices. His mother was the inspiration—and the impetus. Her Scotch and Swedish insistence that the boy must "have an education" was the force that sent him on the road. Few parents had such bravery in that region at that time.

The trombone helped again at Stanford. Summer work was imperative; it was also hard. The pay for labor in the lumber mill that summer of 1927 was 48 cents per hour. Graduation came in June of 1929 and the hardest part was over, for fellowships and teaching assistantships came to the rescue in the graduate years.

The Stanford records show a B— average for the two years of undergraduate work, but nothing less than an A in laboratory work. The graduate years at Stanford were highly successful. Monroe Spaght's research work proceeded successfully, and academic honors and distinctions came freely.

It was unusual for someone so young to have such a keen grasp of scientific matters and he easily won a fellowship from the Institute of International Education to study physics at the University of Leipzig in Germany. Finally, to complete his formal program of education, he returned to Stanford and in 1933 earned a Ph.D. degree.

His last months of Ph.D. work at Stanford, after returning from Germany, were supported by a fellowship granted by the Shell Development Company. (He was to be the president of that company seventeen years later.) The Shell Fellowship at that time was the largest, money-wise, in the university: $900 for a year of study.

When a Shell Oil representative came to the Stanford campus in the spring of 1933 to hire a research chemist, it was the first job opportunity that the Department of Chemistry had seen in years. That Dr. Spaght was offered a job by Shell (at the good salary of $150 per month) had no relationship with the fact that he had held their fellowship.

So far as his career aspirations were concerned, young Dr. Spaght was interested in doing pure research.

"Practical research didn't interest me," he later recalled, "I was going to be an ivory-tower scientist."

His decision to join Shell Oil Company led him to see things differently. He soon discovered that business can afford ivory-tower scientists only if they come up with ideas that will increase company profits. The stockholders who own a corporation are not interested in supporting scientists who concentrate on pure research that does not contribute to the profitable operation of the business. Nevertheless, as we shall see, there *is* a place for the ivory-tower scientist in industry provided he comes up with something worthwhile from time to time.

The Shell Oil Company had had an unusual history that dated back to 1830 when Marcus Samuel started a small Oriental import business in London. His firm prospered and gradually Samuel undertook to own and operate the ships he needed to carry his cargoes. In the early 1890's his sons decided to sell kerosene in addition to their other wares and built one of the first oil tankers to be used to transport crude oil from Baku on the Black Sea to the Far East. This was a radical departure; until then Asia had received most of its kerosene packed in five-gallon cans shipped all the way from Philadelphia or Brooklyn as hold cargo.

The success of the Samuel kerosene venture was immediate, and in October, 1897, it was separated from the rest of their business and incorporated as the "Shell" Transport and Trading Company, Ltd., after the brand name the Samuels had given their kerosene. By 1900 the Shell concern was one of the world's largest oil companies.

Meanwhile in 1883 a Dutch tobacco planter, A. J. Zylker, had discovered natural outcroppings of oil in the wilds of northern Sumatra. After years of inaction, occasioned chiefly by difficulties in raising money, he finally was able to drill wells that were successful enough to prove the profitability of an oil venture in the Indies. In 1890 the Royal Dutch Company for the Working of Petroleum Wells in the Netherlands Indies (shortened in 1949 to Royal Dutch Petroleum Company), with headquarters at The Hague, was organized to take over and operate the oil properties which Zylker had assembled.

Thirteen years later a young Dutchman, H. W. A. Deterding, president of the Royal Dutch Company, promoted an agency through which the leading Far East competitors of the Standard Oil Company could sell their products. The arrangement worked so well that in 1907 a permanent alliance was made between Royal Dutch and the Shell companies. Since that time the Royal Dutch Company and the "Shell" Transport & Trading Company have jointly owned the entire Shell empire of which the Shell Oil Company in the United States is one of many affiliates. This American corporation had its origin not as a single company but in two enterprises founded by the Shell group, a marketing organization on the Pacific Coast, and an oil-producing company in the mid-continent.

The American Gasoline Company was organized in 1912 to market gasoline imported to the Pacific Northwest and San Francisco Bay areas. From the outset the new company operated both through agents and its own depots. The Shell gasoline won ready acceptance because it was of high gravity and worked well in the heavy, hard-to-start engines of that day. Additional water terminals were built and in 1913 the company purchased California Oilfields, Ltd., at Coalinga, one of the largest oil-producing companies in that state. A refinery was built at Martinez and a 170-mile pipeline laid to connect it with the oil fields at Coalinga.

When completed the Martinez refinery set the pattern for all the Shell refineries that were to follow. The old "batch" and "bench" stills, common up to that time, were replaced by a brand-new arrangement—a pipe still, hooked to fractionating towers. This new system could be run continuously with only an occasional closing down for clean-outs, and for the same amount of fuel and investment could turn out larger quantities of petroleum products. Martinez may thus be said to have been the first modern, continuous refinery in America.

Additional refineries and wells were added in California, and in 1929 the Shell Building, a 29-story skyscraper, rose to dominate San Francisco's downtown skyline.

The same year that the American Gasoline Company was founded on the West Coast, the Roxana Petroleum Company of Oklahoma was organized in Tulsa to take over five small oil-producing companies located in northeast Oklahoma. The company quickly added other wells and finally refineries at Cushing, Oklahoma, and Wood River, Illinois, in the St. Louis area. Since 1918, when it went into operation, the Wood River refinery has been Shell's major source of products in the Midwest area. Gradually the company expanded, another marketing company was organized on the Atlantic Coast, and eventually all of the various Shell operations in the United States were consolidated into a single corporation, the Shell Oil Company.

When Dr. Spaght reported for work in 1933 as a research chemist at the Martinez refinery, he began what was to be a 13-year assignment in various aspects of Shell's manufacturing operations. The company was devising a number of important new products and processes—among them several procedures basic to the manufacture of aviation gasoline and a revolutionary new way of manufacturing glycerine and other products by synthesis. In 1935 he was transferred to the Wilmington-Dominiquez refinery as a technologist in the Distilling, Treating and Cracking departments, and later became manager of the Technological Department. He found his research assignments exciting, for it was during this period that he participated in Shell's early work on polymerization (the process of joining two or more like molecules to form a more complex molecule) and hydrogenation (the process of combining or treating with hydrogen), both key processes in the manufacture of aviation gasoline.

Later, looking back on these years when he was so busy working on research projects, Dr. Spaght said: "The rewards for research can be very great indeed, and it is on them that we find our hope of promise for other rewards to come. The way so far is marked with some remarkable achievements, some famous, others obscure. But all are practical.

"The immediate results of basic research are seldom very spectacular. They do not get into the headlines, they do not directly change the lives of millions or result in enormous savings or gains or victories or defeats—not in themselves. But in their longtime effects they may do all these things."

Dr. Irving Langmuir's work in the General Electric Laboratory was one example Dr. Spaght cited. Dr. Langmuir was given freedom to study whatever he wished, and as a result of his experiments the old carbon filament used in light bulbs was replaced with tungsten. Thanks to his discovery, the public was saving over a billion dollars a year as early as 1930.

Another instance was that of a young Harvard instructor, W. H. Carothers, who was hired by E. I. duPont deNemours and Company to begin a program of basic research in organic chemistry. He chose to study polymerization of condensation and the structure of substances of high molecular weight. All of this work led to the discovery of nylon!

A third case mentioned by Dr. Spaght was the basic research done on the electric properties of semiconductors at the Bell Telephone Laboratories which led the research group there to the discovery of the transistor.

Although Dr. Spaght's laboratory investigations did not lead immediately to a spectacular or new discovery, he became recognized as one of the company's foremost scientists and in 1940 was appointed manager of the technological activities of Shell's entire manufacturing operations on the West Coast and moved his office to the Shell Building in San Francisco. With the outbreak of World War II, the armed forces and industry created an immediate and insatiable demand for petroleum products. To help meet this need, Shell undertook an expansion program, building about $30,000,000 worth of manufacturing facilities on the West Coast to increase its gasoline and chemical output.

For Dr. Spaght these were hectic days. It seemed as though there were not enough hours to attend to all the problems that were brought to him. In addition to supervising the building and operating of Shell's West Coast facilities, Dr. Spaght commuted cross-country regularly to Washington, D. C., to serve on a number of government committees. He was an active member of the Ordnance Technical Committee and the Aviation Gasoline Advisory Committee which determined the composition of aviation gasoline that was in such great need throughout the world.

In January of 1945, while our country was still at war with Japan, Dr. Spaght was sent to Europe as a member of the United States Naval Technical Mission to discover what the German chemical and oil industries had developed during the war. While he was abroad Japan surrendered and no sooner had Dr. Spaght returned from his European mission than the government appointed him director of the U. S. Strategic Bombing Survey of Japan to study the effects of our strategic bombing of Japanese industry.

Such outstanding service to both his company and the nation earned Dr. Spaght a new appointment upon his return to the United States in 1946. In an industry that places such emphasis on research, he was the logical choice for vice-president of the Shell Development Company (an affiliate of the Shell Oil Company devoted to research) and but three years later in 1949 was elected its president. On coming into this new assignment Dr. Spaght commented that to a Shell operations man he must have appeared to be a scientist whereas to a scientist he undoubtedly seemed like an operations man. Actually, by this time he had proven his abilities both as a first-rate scientist and as an able operations man and was now being given opportunity to learn something about the administrative end of the business as he directed Shell's huge research program.

During a recent year Shell spent more than $50,000,000 on research as the company sought to develop new products as well as improve existing ones. Although oil and gasoline have always been its most important products, thanks to its research laboratories Shell manufactures a host of other items such as benzene, fertilizers, resins, insecticides, sulphur, glycerine and synthetic rubber. At one time, Dr. Spaght estimated that a third of all Shell's research was devoted to gasoline. Few motorists realize that no two companies make or sell exactly the same gasoline, and that ordinary gas contains more than 1,500 separate components. Never satisfied with what it is marketing today, Shell's researchers are constantly searching for ways to improve what it is making.

In 1953, Dr. Spaght mounted the next step of the corporate ladder when he was elected executive vice-president of the Shell Oil Company. In this position he not only served as deputy to the president in coordinating the parent company and Shell Chemical and Shell Development companies, but he also held executive responsibilities for various major departments of Shell Oil. Eight years later on January 1, 1961, at the age of fifty-one, Monroe E. Spaght was chosen president of Shell Oil Company, becoming what he himself described as "a scientist turned businessman." Trained by education and experience to unravel the complexity of industrial technology and to administer its operations, Dr. Spaght was now top man of this gigantic industrial enterprise.

Although he is an extremely busy man, a continuing study of a wide range of subjects is one of Dr. Spaght's leisure-time occupations. His method is to organize his material by taking one field at a time and reading widely in it. Thus, when he wanted to "know what geologists are talking about," he studied geology exclusively for a period. This new window to the world—geology—combined with his boyhood love of the outdoors, led him to spend five summer vacations in a row in the Arctic. These trips included living with Eskimos, fishing for arctic charr, hunting caribou in the Yukon, and a 300-mile canoe trip down the Albany River west of Hudson Bay.

Probably it was Dr. Spaght's own personal realization of the value of education that prompted him to become one of the leading spokesmen for industry on the problems and progress of education in the United States. He has given much of his free time to work as a trustee of Stanford University, as a director of the Stanford Research Institute, and a director of the Institute of International Education. His concern with education is also reflected in his work as president of the Shell Companies Foundation, Inc. The foundation, among other philanthropic work, has pioneered in introducing new programs in support of education, including fellowships for high school science and mathematics teachers.

In addition to his concern for education, Dr. Spaght is vitally interested in the self-development of Shell employees to their full potential. Once he left a sickbed to give a scheduled talk before the Shell Management Course. Using only a single sheet of notes, he made a full day's presentation on Shell's concept of organization and management practices.

In 1962 he was elected president of the Society of Chemical Industry, an English-based professional society with chapters in many countries. He is the eighth American so honored in this society's history.

Dr. Spaght believes that the modern corporation has a very important role in society.

"A company's management is responsible today, not merely to thousands or hundreds of thousands of stockholders, but also to thousands of employees, to multiplied thousands of their dependents, and to still more people in the communities where the company operates and its suppliers operate. It must be stable. It must be progressive. So it must look to the future for itself and for all who depend upon it."

Whether you look forward to becoming an ivory-tower scientist or a practical researcher, Dr. Spaght believes that your goal should be to serve your fellow men. "Companies spend money on research with hope of eventual profit," he said. "This hope rests on the certainty that profit comes only from service to society. Basic research, which broadens industry's knowledge far beyond its immediate goals, has served us well in the past and is serving us magnificently now. We have no choice but to foster its growth for still greater service in the future."

The intensive training Dr. Spaght received prior to joining Shell prepared him for a technical, not a well-rounded business, career. Nevertheless his later ability to direct the three chief activities of the company—technical, operational and administrative—was proof that science as an occupation does not necessarily mean a lifetime in the research laboratory. As in Dr. Spaght's case, the scientist too can rise to the very top.

The citation to an honorary D.Sc. from Drexel Institute of Technology in 1962 recalled that Sir Francis Bacon had said, "Knowledge should bear fruit in works and science has its ultimate validity in its practical application through technology to improve the lot of mankind." The citation termed Dr. Spaght "an industrial scientist in the best Baconian tradition."

Chapter 8

•

THE BRAVE MOUNTAIN
CLIMBER

"TO be blunt, Dr. Cox," the government official was saying, "the United States Public Health Service wants you to leave the Rockefeller Institute and join the Service. You'll go out to our Hamilton laboratory in Montana and see what you can do to find a safer and more efficient way to make vaccine for Rocky Mountain spotted fever."

Dr. Herald Cox, who was only twenty-nine at the time, hesitated for a moment. He thought of his wife and two children, for he knew that Rocky Mountain spotted fever had already claimed six of its fighters. Existing vaccine was made by grinding up millions of the tiny infected wood ticks which carried the disease. It was no secret that this would be an extremely dangerous task, for any slight miscalculation meant possible death to the man working on a vaccine.

"I'll go," the young scientist said quietly. For the next two years he worked steadily, day and night, on a task that proved so difficult and discouraging that he finally considered resigning. Dr. Cox knew that if he could get the disease-causing agent to grow in egg tissue (chick embryo tissue) there would no longer be any need to use the dangerous live ticks. All previous attempts to grow the rickettsiae* in quantity in living chick embryo tissue had failed.

"I've spent two years here without making any progress," he told Dr. Ralph R. Parker, who had helped develop the Spencer-Parker vaccine then in use. "I think I should resign and let someone else try his hand."

"Don't get discouraged yet," Dr. Parker said. "I've been fighting these wood ticks for sixteen years and still I'm not ready to quit."

One day, less than a month later, Dr. Cox was unable to find enough chick embryo tissue to make up his cultures. Because of this shortage he minced up the membrane surrounding the yolk of the egg and used it instead of the embryonic chick tissue inside. Six days later the makeshift culture swarmed with easily harvestable rickettsiae.

It was the yolk sac tissue that did it! Researchers had grown viruses in the various tissues of the chick embryo and its surrounding membranes. Previously scattered efforts had been made to grow viruses in the embryo's food instead of in the embryo itself. Injection of the rickettsiae into the yolk sac membrane of the living egg succeeded whereas efforts to grow it in all other parts of the fertile egg had failed.

Virologists and bacteriologists showered Dr. Cox with honors. In 1940 a leading university offered him its chair of bacteriology. The U. S. Public Health Service promoted him to its top scientific rank, Principal Bacteriologist, to retain him. At thirty-three he became the youngest top-

---

* Microorganisms that are causative agents of certain diseases such as Rocky Mountain spotted fever, epidemic (or louse-borne) typhus fever and Q fever.

ranking scientist in the long history of the U. S. Public Health Service. In 1941 Dr. Irving Langmuir, president of the American Association for the Advancement of Science, presented Dr. Cox with the coveted Theobald Smith Award in the Medical Sciences.

Herald Rea Cox, the son of Pauline Mae Rea and Lee Robert Cox, was born on a farm near Rosedale, Indiana, on February 28, 1907. His father, who had worked for the New York Central Railroad until partially blinded in one eye by an accident, was a mechanic. Herald, the oldest child, had two brothers and a sister.

"When I was in the fourth grade I failed arithmetic," he recalled. "I had to work so hard to pass that second examination that instead of disliking the subject I became deeply interested in it, and my love for math later influenced my lifework."

When he was only eleven he had his first paper route, and from that day until he graduated from college he supported himself and paid all of his school expenses with earnings from delivering newspapers. History, one of Herald's chief interests in Garfield High at Terre Haute, Indiana, won him a medal, and he found chemistry so fascinating that he led his class in that subject with a 99 average.

In 1924 he entered Indiana State College. Within his first three years there he took all of the mathematics courses the college offered. Where most students have one major, Herald had three: mathematics, physics and chemistry. Little wonder he was elected president of the college honorary scientific society! Instead of vacationing during July and August he attended summer school and in his junior year switched jobs to a morning newspaper, building up the largest paper route in the state. Every morning he worked from quarter of two until six-thirty, riding his bike some 23 miles to make certain that his 470 customers had their morning papers in time to read them at breakfast.

Because all seniors at Indiana State were required to do some practice teaching, Herald taught chemistry and mathematics to the senior class in the nearby high school. One of his students, Marion A. Curry, took an immediate liking to him and they became friends, but his life was then too busy for any serious romance.

After graduation from Indiana State in 1928 Herald went to Johns Hopkins University on an Eli Lilly fellowship to continue his scientific training. Here he took his first course in biology (human anatomy) and immediately a new world opened to him. Thanks to his interest in mathematics, he became intrigued with the problem of devising a filtration method for measuring the size of viruses, and he used this research as the basis for his doctorate's thesis.

"Although I received my Doctor of Science degree in hygiene with specialization in viruses, my thesis had to be approved by both the mathematics and physics departments of the Homewood Campus of the university before it would be accepted," he explained. He found this study so fascinating that he decided to study viruses as individual entities.

It has become fashionable during the last few years to blame every stubborn or unknown infection on a "virus." A virus may be defined as a disease-producing microbe, smaller than ordinary bacteria, which cannot reproduce outside the right kind of living cell. More than 200 different viruses have been identified but we only know many of them by the diseases they cause in plants, animals or man. Most viruses are smaller than the visible wavelength of light. The head of a pin, for instance, is large enough to hold 25 million of the viruses which cause polio.

The invention of the electron microscope in 1938 has enabled virologists to see the magnified shadow produced when a virus deflects a bombardment of electrons. Although this helped virologists discover some elusive microbes, it did not help identify unknown viruses—first one must catch the individual organism before it can be magnified by the electron microscope.

After receiving his Sc.D. in 1931, Dr. Cox remained at Johns Hopkins to work with Doctors Perrin Long and Roscoe R. Hyde on the cause of the common cold. At the same time he became an instructor in virology and immunology and was making more frequent trips to Terre Haute to visit brunette Marion Curry, who by that time had become a schoolteacher.

Dr. Cox married Marion Curry on June 19, 1932, and in September joined the Rockefeller Institute for Medical Research in New York City. Here he worked under the famed bacteriologist Peter K. Olitsky, and developed killed vaccines against eastern and western equine encephalomyelitis. After spending four years with the institute he joined the U. S. Public Health Service and made his now famous discovery that rickettsiae could be grown in the yolk sac of the developing chick embryo. During this period two of his three children, Jane and George, were born.

Next Dr. Cox began to screen other viruses and rickettsiae to see which would respond favorably to the same treatment. One of the rickettsiae Dr. Cox tested was the agent of epidemic typhus fever. Until recently this epidemic disease, which is carried by a body louse, had killed literally millions of soldiers and decimated populations caught in the filth of war. It has been stated that typhus has done more to change the course of history than any weapons forged by man. Dr. Cox's experiments in the Hamilton

Laboratory were to change all this sooner than anyone imagined.

With most of Europe already fighting and with war clouds looming over the United States, there was no time to lose. Far into the night Dr. Cox worked steadily in the laboratory, determined to perfect his typhus vaccine. If war came he wanted to have ready an effective means of preventing typhus epidemics.

Shortly after the Japanese struck at Pearl Harbor on December 7, 1941, a group of American and Canadian army surgeons met secretly to see what could be done to eliminate the threat of typhus.

"If one of the new insecticides can kill lice it will wipe out typhus," one surgeon suggested.

"What about vaccinating both soldiers and civilians?" asked another.

"That's the only effective way to control typhus," a third doctor declared, and the others quickly agreed with him. Vaccine was the answer, but how could it be made and where?

It was known that a Polish laboratory was making about 5,000 doses of typhus vaccine a year by grinding up infected lice fed on human beings who had recovered from typhus. The army physicians agreed that this method would never produce the quantities of vaccine that would be needed. It was therefore decided to adopt Dr. Cox's yolk sac method and ask both public and industrial American and Canadian laboratories to make the vaccine in huge quantities. One of the companies engaged in the program, the Lederle Laboratories Division of American Cyanamid Company, had such extensive facilities for manufacturing vaccine that they were requested to make half the quantity assigned to industrial laboratories.

The Lederle Laboratories date back to the turn of the century when, as a young man, Dr. Ernst J. Lederle established a laboratory for chemical and bacteriological analyses in a New York City loft. He served as health commissioner of New York City in 1902 and 1903 and during this time an improvement in the method of refining diphtheria antitoxin was developed.

After Dr. Lederle left the Health Department in 1903 his interest in diphtheria led him to decide that he would manufacture this improved product in his own laboratory. Dr. William H. Park, at that time director of the New York City Research Laboratories, became associated with Dr. Lederle in this venture.

These men were successful in their first efforts, and it soon became apparent that a separate manufacturing organization was necessary if a large quantity of the new antitoxin was to be prepared and marketed. As a result, the Lederle Antitoxin Laboratories were established at Pearl River, New York, in 1906. At first the only item produced by Lederle was diphtheria antitoxin, but gradually there was a broadening of the field to include tetanus antitoxin, typhoid vaccine, and other bacterial and viral vaccines for medical use.

In the early 1920's the laboratories expanded in both production and personnel. By 1922 some 450 people were working and producing such products as pituitary extract, epinephrine solution, desiccated thyroid tablets and digitalis products. In 1930 American Cyanamid Company purchased the Lederle Antitoxin Laboratories and changed the name to Lederle Laboratories, Inc.

Today the Lederle Laboratories consist of more than 150 separate buildings on a vast 600-acre tract in Pearl River. Almost a city in itself, it has its own maintenance department for the 18 miles of streets and sidewalks, its own fire department, ambulance, dispensary, social clubs and recreation facilities. About 5,000 employees are engaged in research, production and distribution of more than 350 pharmaceutical and biological products supplied in nearly a thousand package forms. Much of this growth took place since the beginning of World War II in 1942 when that first order for epidemic typhus vaccine was received.

Those in charge of the laboratories were stunned when they learned what was expected of them. Anxious to meet the production quota assigned to their laboratories, the management persuaded Dr. Cox to come and take charge of the typhus vaccine program and also direct a virus research program for the company.

In no time the laboratories were humming with activity. Assembly lines, manned by men and women wearing spotless white uniforms, were turning out dozens of vials of vaccine. Seven days a week trucks rolled up to the receiving dock to unload 12,000 eggs a day for typhus vaccine production. Scientists worked around the clock growing and preparing typhus vaccine from the infected eggs.

The vaccine proved itself under fire. It checked a threatened typhus epidemic in North Africa and another in Greece. It was administered to several million American, Canadian and Allied troops who were sent to areas where they might be exposed to typhus. Civilian populations in certain danger zones were given the vaccine, which reduced the mortality from typhus to practically zero.

The war kept the Viral and Rickettsial Research Section hopping from one emergency to another. At one time Lederle used an additional 33,000 eggs a day, six days a week, for flu vaccine alone. With an invasion of Japan in mind, the Army asked Lederle to work out a protection against Japanese B encephalitis, a viral fever which has killed 8,000 residents of the Japanese islands in a single epidemic year. The vaccine was originally produced from infected brain tissue of twelve- to fourteen-day-old white mice, and in order to meet the Army's requirements, Lederle was using 6,000 mice a day, six days a week, for Japanese B vaccine production alone.

During World War II, the laboratories supplied 33 percent of all the typhus vaccine used by the armed forces, 50 percent of the gas gangrene antitoxin, all of the blood grouping sera, 33 percent of the influenza virus vaccine, 90 percent of the pneumonia sera, 25 percent of the blood plasma, 40 percent of the Japanese B encephalitis vaccine, and half of the tetanus toxoid.

One thing the war experience made clear was that virus vaccine production could not be separated from virus research. Strains of viruses are too fickle to be routinized. Contamination with bacteria, to say nothing of the danger of infection to lab workers, could best be combated when the entire process was under research direction. Moreover the potency and stability of the vaccine and unusual reactions to it have to be watched closely even after the vaccine is standardized.

As was true in many fields, Lederle recognized that the heroic days of easy discovery had passed in virus research. One brilliant mind working alone could no longer hope to attain significant results. The problems left unsolved were left unsolved precisely because their complexity required the association of many different skills and scientific disciplines. Accordingly, Dr. Cox set about acquiring a staff which would work as a team: biochemists to study the host-virus relationship; pathologists to study the disease-producing influence of viruses on cells; physical chemists; and biologists.

Medical research support by private industry has contributed greatly to our welfare. However, dollars cannot do the job without brains coupled with unselfish devotion to the job. Men, as always, must come before bricks and mortar. Lederle chose them not for their accomplishments or their interests at the moment, but for their patience in the unglamorous pursuit of limited objectives, their honesty in assessing their own results, and their willingness to cooperate with others. Most of the men sought were teaching in universities or doing research in hospitals, in government agencies, or in privately endowed foundations.

A generation ago many scientists looked disdainfully at industrial pharmaceutical firms. This attitude has changed. "In the past few years scientists have come to realize that you do just as good work in an industrial laboratory as in a university," Dr. Cox said.

Science knows no nationality. The virus staff that Dr. Cox helped assemble for Lederle was composed of men from all over the world. There was Dr. James van der Scheer, a native of Padang, Netherlands East Indies, who had been a research chemist working on antigens, immunology and related serum problems before coming to Lederle. Twenty-eight-year-old Dr. Hilary Koprowski, a graduate of the medical school of Warsaw, Poland, had spent the war years working on problems of the yellow fever virus in Rio de Janeiro. There was Dr. Floyd S. Markham of Ohio State University, who had met Dr. Cox at Montana in the Hamilton laboratory, Dr. Victor Cabasso from France and Tunisia, and Dr. Manuel Roca-García from Bogotá, Colombia, South America.

All these men were skilled and conscientious researchers. Together, their varying backgrounds and training made them a strong team to tame living viruses that would produce cheaper, safer, and longer-lasting vaccines than the killed vaccines then in wide use. Dr. Cox and his staff solved a number of problems in human and veterinary medicine. In the veterinary field they developed vaccines for hog cholera, Newcastle disease and infectious bronchitis in chickens, rabies, canine distemper and canine hepatitis among others. It was estimated that the hog cholera vaccine alone saved U. S. farmers approximately $250 million a year. In human medicine they conducted extensive research on vaccines against measles, mumps, infectious hepatitis and rabies, as well as polio. At the same time they investigated the viral implications of certain cancers.

One of the antibiotics developed in the Lederle Laboratories was a material made from a mold that had been isolated from a spadeful of dirt taken from the University of Missouri where Dr. Benjamin Duggar, head of the antibiotics laboratory, had once taught. Because of its golden yellow color the drug was called Aureomycin. It was designated A-377, and proved effective against more than 50 different germ species including the rickettsiae of Rocky Mountain spotted fever, epidemic typhus and Q fever, and some large viruslike agents. Because he was an expert on Rocky Mountain spotted fever, Dr. Cox was asked to test it in his laboratory against the causative agent of the fever. Dr. Cox soon found that the new drug quickly cured guinea pigs which had been infected with the disease.

On June 16, 1948, Dr. Cox received an urgent telephone call.

"We need your help, Dr. Cox," the voice on the other end pleaded. "There's a ten-year-old boy here in the hospital who has a bad case of what we believe is Rocky Mountain spotted fever. For a week he's run a high temperature, had severe headaches, muscle pains, and for the last five days a rash has covered his body. Can you come over?"

"Of course! I'll be right there."

When he joined the doctors gathered about the bed, Dr. Cox learned that the boy's temperature was 104.6 degrees and that he was in a coma. After a hurried consultation it was decided to try the new drug as a last resort, even though it had not yet been tested on humans. Within 36 hours the boy's temperature had dropped to normal and on June 19th Dr. Cox noted that "the patient has made tremendous improvement." A week after he first received the drug the boy left the hospital, the first spotted fever case to receive Aureomycin, and one of the first persons to receive Aureomycin.

In 1952 Dr. Cox realized his dream of many years, a new Virus Building, the design of which incorporated several of his ideas. From the front the brick building looks deceptively small, but the animal quarters which occupy an L-shaped annex are as long as the façade. The animal rooms are so well hidden (at the joint of the L there is an air lock to block out animal odors) that a visitor going up the broad steps to the main entrance could easily mistake the building for a new public library or school.

Once inside the modern glass doors, the unsuspecting outsider notices the neatness of the green tile walls and the composition flooring. There is no place for dust to hide. Everywhere it is very quiet—almost unnaturally restful.

The absence of normal messengers and traffic accounts for part of it, the dropped acoustical tile ceilings which hide all pipes and ducts help too.

Safety, as well as convenience, is built into the layout. The basement is devoted to production; administrative offices and a few special laboratories are on the first floor; the second and third floors contain the research laboratories. The laboratories themselves have been likened to a scientist's dream of what a research laboratory should be. Work areas are isolated from one another, there are ample benches, and services (gas, electricity, oxygen) are located on a ledge to permit easier cleaning of the work space. Working surfaces are of a carbonized birch and soapstone and contrast decoratively with the green tile walls. Lights, fixtures, in fact everything possible, are flush and sealed for freedom from dust. Operating rooms for autopsies on animals are equipped with hospital lights and all facilities for antiseptic procedures. Storage of viruses and cultures is provided for in two cold rooms in which proper temperatures are maintained.

Here each month the Virus and Rickettsial Research Section uses approximately 20,000 mice, 200 hamsters, 1,200 rats, 1,700 chickens, 200 guinea pigs, and 25 rabbits. Not only are 2,000 fertile eggs needed every week for research alone, but there are also some 200 rhesus monkeys on hand and facilities to keep 300 more. Little wonder the research scientists associated with Dr. Cox welcomed their new building with enthusiasm.

One medical problem that haunted Dr. Cox and his associates was polio, the crippling and killing disease for which there was no cure when Dr. Cox first considered the matter in 1945.

"We tackled polio because it was a grave problem and

represented a scientific challenge," Dr. Cox said when re-calling those early days. "We're sort of mountain climbers in that respect; our work is never done, there's always another peak to conquer."

The Lederle researchers believed that the possibility of immunizing man against poliomyelitis with a modified or weakened living virus probably offered the best chance of success. The most successful vaccines such as those against smallpox and yellow fever were made from living weakened microbes, not from dead ones.

In 1950 a live weakened polio virus had been developed which was to be given orally. Dr. Cox insisted on being among the first to take this vaccine in order to test the safety of the product. He experienced no adverse reaction. Dr. Hilary Koprowski, Dr. Cox's assistant, then fed the virus to 85 young volunteers in Sonoma, California. Every-one who took the preventive vaccine became immune, none were harmed. Apparently after the Cox vaccine is taken orally, immunity begins within a few days in the alimentary canal, where the polio virus normally first establishes itself and grows.

Next came the seemingly endless job of testing the vac-cine to prove its safety and effectiveness. During this period the Salk vaccine, which was made from killed polio virus, made its appearance and was widely accepted and admin-istered. Nevertheless Dr. Cox and his associates pushed ahead to prove the value of their vaccine. In 1957 at the University of Minnesota's department of pediatrics, it was fed to 25 babies and almost all responded with immunity in their blood to the three types of polio virus received. The following year 7,000 children in Andes County, Colombia, South America, were given the vaccine when a polio epidemic exploded there. The results were startling, and later all children under ten years of age in Medellín, Colombia, as well as in Managua, the capital of Nicaragua, received the vaccine. No paralytic polio appeared there during the next year although up to that time numerous cases had been experienced regularly.

Soon many South American countries were begging for the vaccine. Every dose was provided free by Lederle since it had not yet been licensed for sale by the U. S. Public Health Service. According to an article that appeared in the *New England Journal of Medicine* in 1960, many leading virologists and epidemiologists agreed that lasting immunity against polio can be achieved only by administering a living virus that will reach and grow in the alimentary canal.

The vaccine's manufacturing process, as required by the National Institutes of Health regulations, calls for a minimum of four to six months for the completion of each batch. Approximately three-fourths of this time and effort is devoted to testing procedures carried out upon the vaccine to prove its sterility and safety. In obtaining a license for the general manufacture and distribution of an oral vaccine Lederle Laboratories had to submit 15 consecutive batches (five for each of the three types of polio) to the government for evaluation.

In addition, Lederle conducted tightly controlled clinical studies among susceptible individuals with each of the 15 batches of vaccine to determine its immunizing power as well as to help establish the dosage. Such testing required at least three to six months of time. Results of these studies were then sent to Washington as part of the license application.

Commenting on the time it took to get the vaccine accepted, Dr. Cox said, "We certainly didn't think it would take thirteen years when we started our work, but we've learned a lot since then. And we hope that we'll be wiser when we move on to our next mountain."

Herald Cox is a scientist's scientist. A quiet man whose few words convey a deep belief in his work, he consults with his associates as a fellow worker, not as a boss. It was his knowledge, strength and dedication that directed his team through the 13-year polio vaccine search in spite of numerous dead ends along the way and many attacks on his theory from outside sources. His experience back at the Hamilton laboratory when he thought of giving up taught him the necessity for "climbing to the top of every mountain" in the quest for medical progress. Thus it was his belief that an oral vaccine would provide more lasting protection for less cost against polio than the Salk vaccine that convinced Cyanamid his work must go on, no matter what the cost.

Dr. Cox is an outdoor man. His idea of a perfect vacation is a hunting or fishing trip to Montana.

"I wish I could get away more often," he said wistfully, "but in the past few years our polio research problems have kept me pretty well glued to the Pearl River laboratories. Now that we're working on measles and rubella (German measles) it's the same story."

Keeping his four acres of green lawn mowed is almost a full-time second job. Reading is another activity for Dr. Cox. "Anyone in research must do a tremendous amount of reading," he said. "It is important to know what everyone else is doing." Some travel is required, both within and without the United States. Dr. Cox visits other laboratories and also checks on work in progress at other research installations partially supported by Lederle funds.

The inability to get away to Montana as often as he

would like is partially compensated for by the fun of living near his daughter, son-in-law, and four lively grandchildren. Both of his sons are doctors. His oldest son, George, is a resident in medicine at the University of Wisconsin. The younger boy, Gordon, received his M.D. degree in June, 1963.

As long as disease attacks mankind there will always be the challenge of "another mountain to be conquered," even at the risk of death, for men like Dr. Cox. To such men each of us owes a tremendous debt of gratitude.

Chapter 9

•

THE IMAGINATIVE ENGINEER

O NE day during the summer of 1948 three young house-wives took their places in triangle formation at the center of a field near Hartford, Connecticut. Holding a ply-wood square on her head each faced toward the *Life* maga-zine photographer. Overhead hovered a helicopter carrying a test pilot and one passenger, the husband of Helen Kaman, one of the girls. Slowly the machine descended and gently touched its wheels on the three plywood squares. The camera clicked and then the craft gracefully regained altitude and flew away, completing a dramatic demonstration of the safety and maneuverability of the K-190. This was the in-vention of Charles Kaman, who was then only twenty-nine and the head of the Kaman Aircraft Corporation which had some two dozen employees.

Mr. Kaman's helicopter was of unusual design, controlled by simple flaps on its rotor blades instead of the compli-cated mechanisms found on conventional helicopters. The K-190 could safely execute a breathtakingly sharp turn about the top of a tall chimney or cruise easily at 75 miles an hour at an altitude of 11,000 feet. More important, it was so simple to handle that Ann Griffin, one of the three fearless young ladies, made her solo flight after only 36 minutes of instruction in the air.

Today Kaman Aircraft is a leading manufacturer of helicopters. How it grew from a one-man organization to a major industrial enterprise that employs almost 5,000 men and women—all within the short span of about fifteen years—is really the story of Charles Kaman, its tall, good-looking president, the company's founder and guiding genius.

Charles W. Kaman (pronounced Ka-*Man*), the son of Charles W. Kaman and Mabel Davis Kaman, was born in Washington, D. C., on June 15, 1919. His father, a civil engineer, was in the construction business, and his firm erected many of the hotels and office buildings in and around the nation's capital. When Mr. Kaman proudly pointed out the buildings to his small son, young Charlie's gaze was directed not at the structures but at the sky above them in the hope that he would see an airplane. From an early age the boy was fascinated by airplanes and his interest increased as he grew older.

"From the time I was six until I went to college I built and flew model planes," he said. "When I was seven I won my first prize with a forty-five-second flight. By the time I graduated from high school our little planes were staying up for as long as twenty-one minutes."

The contests were tests of endurance, and during these years Charlie's engineering abilities were amply demonstrated as he learned how to build airplanes that would fly longer than any of the others. Years later his same flair for making design improvements would be dignified with the term "imaginative engineering."

"Some of my planes ended up in the rafters of an auditorium, a gymnasium or an armory," he recalled later. "In fact I once flew one to the top of Constitution Hall!"

Aviation was not his only interest. He was a good student and enjoyed sports and parties. Another important hobby was his music, and for several years he studied the guitar, at one time joining a group of friends to form a little band. By the time he graduated from Roosevelt High School, he had become a proficient performer. By chance Tommy Dorsey, the famous band leader, happened to hear young Kaman and was so impressed with his ability that he offered him a job in his orchestra. This was a tempting offer, with the prospect of no more studying, little hard work, and a lot of fun playing his favorite instrument. It was not an easy decision, but Charlie's love of aviation and interest in aerodynamics won over his fondness for music. He decided to keep music as his avocation and enter college to become an engineer. Accordingly he enrolled at Catholic University because it offered the specialty he wanted and would enable him to live at home. By this time the depression had hit the construction business and Charlie's father could not easily afford to send his son away to school where he would have to pay for room and board.

In 1940 Charles Kaman, *magna cum laude,* was one of six to graduate with a B.S. in Aeronautical Engineering. He lost no time taking the first plane to Hartford, Connecticut, to join the Hamilton Standard Division of the United Aircraft Corporation. Here he was assigned to the rotary wing group which was working on helicopters.

The helicopter traces its history back to 1483 when Leonardo da Vinci sketched a rotating corkscrew fan designed to produce direct lift. Although many men toyed with the idea over the next 400 years, it was not until 1907 that Paul Cornu raised a helicopter five feet above the ground for one moment. In 1910 Igor I. Sikorsky piloted his first helicopter in Kiev, Russia. He soon became famous as a builder of multi-engine flying boats and amphibians for over-ocean travel, organized his original Sikorsky Aero Engineering Corp. in 1923, and in 1934 sold his company (then known as Sikorsky Aviation Corp.) to United Aircraft Corporation. In 1939 he made his initial flight in the VS-300, the first successful single main rotor helicopter in the world. Two years later he established an endurance record of over an hour and a half. In December of 1940 the government authorized the Vought-Sikorsky Division of the United Aircraft Corporation to develop a new two-place, side-by-side helicopter.

The helicopter intrigued young Mr. Kaman and within a comparatively short time he had published a paper in which he demonstrated the applications of basic aerodynamic theories to helicopter design. This proved an important breakthrough of that day and he was placed in charge of the section that was studying helicopter aerodynamics.

For Charles Kaman life was not all work in the office, however. There was still the guitar, and more important there was Helen Sylvander. A native of Coraopolis, Pennsylvania, this vivacious girl had graduated from Penn State and obtained a job at United Aircraft in the drafting department. Here she and Charles Kaman met over the drawing board and soon, whenever time permitted, they were seeing more and more of each other.

One day he had an inspiration for a revolutionary new kind of helicopter control system. With his usual gusto and enthusiasm he went right to work on it. Night after night he spent many hours reading, studying, figuring and sketching as he worked on his idea. Again and again he checked his data to make certain it was aerodynamically feasible and not just another drawing-board theory which would prove impractical when translated into a working model.

When he was absolutely satisfied that he was on the right track he organized the "Kaman Aircraft Laboratory" in order to have a formal organization through which he could raise money and obtain the scarce metals and parts he needed. Some of these were unobtainable without a priority order certifying that they were required to further the war effort. After he managed to talk Grover Loening of the War Production Board into granting him a priority, he cleaned out the cellar of his mother's West Hartford home and converted it into a combination laboratory and factory.

Next, using his own funds plus some money contributed by interested friends, he purchased a 1933 Pontiac engine, mounted it on a two-wheel rig so that it could be moved from place to place, and proceeded to build a test rig.

Every test proved Mr. Kaman's theories on rotors, and as he continued to work with the rig he was able to extend and further develop his ideas. It was 1945 and, now that the war was over, he was anxious to do something with his invention. It seemed logical to offer it to United Aircraft, but to his surprise the company evidenced no interest. Who was Charles Kaman, a young man of twenty-six compared to the great Igor I. Sikorsky, the helicopter expert?

Disappointed but not discouraged, Mr. Kaman made two important decisions. He would leave United Aircraft and start his own company, renaming it the Kaman Aircraft Corporation, and he would ask Helen Sylvander to marry him. His total assets consisted of the test rig into which he had poured so much effort and $2,000 savings which he had accumulated while working at Hamilton Standard. The prospects of competing successfully in the helicopter field against United Aircraft Corporation and other well-financed and experienced companies were very dim. Nor were his chances good for obtaining additional money to continue research and build the first helicopter.

The very fact that the future looked so dubious was a challenge this young couple wanted to face together— and conquer. On October 20, 1945, they were married, eager to share for better or worse whatever the coming years might hold. Two months later they saw the Kaman Aircraft Corporation officially organized.

Mr. Kaman soon discovered that it is one thing to work out the details of an invention and quite another to handle the hundreds of details that must precede the manufacture of the first prototype. In this respect his situation was quite different from that of most of the other engineers and scientists discussed in this book. They were employed by corporations which not only paid their salaries but provided everything needed for research and development, thus leaving them free to concentrate all their attention on their work. Mr. Kaman, however, had practically nothing with which to work and during the next several years the task of raising money would be one of his greatest problems.

Mr. Kaman's entire early effort was aimed at testing the validity of his two theories. One of these was his invention, the servoflap-control system, small aileron-type flaps located on the trailing edge of each rotor blade. These flaps allowed aerodynamic forces to do most of the work by changing the pitch of the blade and replaced complicated mechanisms used to control conventional helicopters. The result was a far more stable helicopter and "fingertip" ease of control, a kind of aerodynamic power steering which takes advantage of existing natural forces.

The second design difference from conventional helicopters was the twin-intermeshing rotor configuration or "synchropter." The intermeshing rotor eliminated need for a tail rotor, inherently overcoming the problem of torque, the tendency of the aircraft to spin in a direction opposite the rotation of the rotor. Another advantage was an increase in available power since the tail rotor generally required up to 10 percent of engine horsepower. Helicopters of this design were found to possess greater lifting power per engine horsepower than single rotor designs.

As Mr. Kaman continued to test with his rig he succeeded in convincing the U. S. Navy that his design approach had merit. Soon Navy representatives visited him to see a demonstration.

That night he could hardly wait to tell Mrs. Kaman the good news.

"Guess what! We're really in business! The Navy's going to give us a $15,000 contract for a rotor system and they're going to ask the National Advisory Committee on Aeronautics to test it!"

A government contract—$15,000—real interest in his design. He had good cause for rejoicing!

Mr. Kaman's initial task was to find more space, and in 1946 he leased an old gymnasium which the Air Force had built at Bradley Field near Hartford. The company's first employee was Bill Murray, a former Navy flight instructor, who was intrigued by the prospect of flying helicopters.

By the end of the year, ten employees were working on the first helicopter designated the K-125 (numerals representing the approximate horsepower).

Meanwhile Mr. Kaman's reputation had spread to Boston and he visited some financiers who represented New Enterprises, a group of Boston venture capitalists. They agreed to invest in the company and provide half of

their investment for a starter. When (and if!) the first helicopter made a successful flight they promised to send the
balance.

By January of 1947 Mr. Kaman was ready to test his
K-125. A crowd gathered at Bradley Field to witness the
event. If Mr. Kaman was nervous he did not show it as the
pilot climbed into the helicopter and took the controls. It
had to work—everything he had done during the past several
years indicated that it should.

There was a low hum as he switched on the engine, then
at his signal most of the ten employees stationed themselves
about the helicopter. As the twin rotors began to whirl, the
men grabbed the aircraft and acting as human tethers—
lest the K-125 shoot suddenly up into the air—hung onto
its sides. The rotors functioned perfectly and lifted the
machine a foot above the ground.

A spontaneous cheer rose from the crowd which had
gathered to witness the first flight and the men jostled each
other as they sought to congratulate their boss. For Mr.
Kaman it was a thrilling moment. He had proved that his
theories were sound, the design correct, and best of all the
working model *worked!* Now New Enterprises would lend
him the rest of the money and, better still, the U. S. Navy
had proof that the K-125 could perform.

After this initial test it was not long before Mr. Kaman,
together with Bill Murray, who had become his test pilot,
could fly their new invention with skill and ease. During
1947 and 1948 the helicopter made numerous demonstra-
tions around the Hartford area. These flights were necessary to test thoroughly the aircraft and certain design
changes, for now Mr. Kaman's group was working hard to
obtain Civil Aeronautics Administration certification. The
company could not sell or fly the helicopter commercially

without the all-important government certification which finally came early in 1949.

The many problems attendant to developing, constructing, and testing a brand-new piece of equipment, plus the responsibility of managing a company, were nothing compared to the perpetual worry of how to meet the weekly payroll. Often Mr. Kaman wondered where the money would come from as he watched the bank balance sink dangerously near zero. Somehow he always managed to find funds.

Friends and relatives put up about $50,000 in return for stock, and a local bank lent him money. On Sunday afternoons his employees would go to Bradley Field and while Bill Murray put the K-125 through every conceivable maneuver, the other men would mix with the crowd to sell shares of Kaman stock to anyone who had some courage— and cash. Later a number of interested Hartford businessmen formed the Kaman Advisory Committee. The men visited the plant, liked what they saw and invested some money.

"Once when we were absolutely down to our last dollar," Mr. Kaman recalled, "I drove to the bank on a Friday afternoon.

" 'This is all I have left,' I told the bank officer as I handed him my savings book. 'Please let me have my $200, there's a payroll to meet tonight.'

" 'Mr. Kaman,' he said, 'keep your savings account. We've got so much invested in your company now, we might as well lend you some more.' "

And so another crisis was met, permitting the engineers and mechanics to continue under Mr. Kaman's direction with the construction of a larger helicopter than the original K-125.

With certification, Mr. Kaman proceeded to build 11

open-cockpit, open-framework helicopters which were designated K-225. They were used that summer in crop-dusting operations from Maine to Florida and earned the company $25,000, the company leasing the machines and sending along its own pilots and mechanics. Helicopters proved especially effective for this work because the power-ful downwash of air distributed the insecticides evenly. Although the $25,000 they earned would be an insignificant sum to most businesses, it provided Mr. Kaman with badly needed cash. Just as important, the summer's work proved the ruggedness of the K-225 helicopter and the effective-ness of the twin-rotor and servoflap designs.

By now the Navy was convinced that the Kaman product was both dependable and maneuverable and it purchased two K-225's for flight evaluation at the Naval Air Test Center at Patuxent River, Maryland. The aircraft passed all its tests so well that Mr. Kaman received a contract in May of 1950 for the design, development and production of the HOK-1, an observation helicopter powered by a piston engine. About this time he was forced to find larger quarters for his expanding company. He arranged to begin construc-tion in 1952 so he could move from the gymnasium to a new plant in nearby Bloomfield.

This opened a new era for the company, an era which produced the first profit for Mr. Kaman: $27,000 on sales of $4,800,000 in 1951. During that same year a Kaman K-225 powered by a Boeing gas turbine engine took to the air to become the world's first turbine-powered helicopter. (The U. S. Navy has since presented the K-225 to the Smithsonian Institution in Washington. This turborotor helicopter is the original example of the twin intermeshing rotor type aircraft on display in the Smithsonian.)

In 1952 Kaman helicopters were delivered to the U. S. Navy and started operating with the Atlantic fleet, while the following year Mr. Kaman and his engineers began work on a remote-control helicopter. Directed by radio signals from a station on the ground, the robot helicopter flew and landed with the same precision and ease as piloted craft. Next the Army became interested in what Mr. Kaman's company was doing and, with the Navy, sponsored the world's first twin-turbine HTK helicopter.

The new-found success did not diminish the pioneering imagination and enthusiasm which had characterized the company's early years. At this point in his career Mr. Kaman could have been content to follow his friends' advice, take things easier and spend more time at home. His helicopter was a success, he operated in a large modern plant, the company had fine government contracts and was providing steady employment for many people in the area. It was not his nature, though, to sit back and do nothing. He thrives on projects that would challenge his ingenuity and ever-active imagination. Mr. Kaman felt impelled to pool his scientific training and knowledge with that of his technicians to see what they could develop working as a team.

A logical extension of the Kaman helicopter was the Rotochute, first developed for the Marine Corps to drop food or bombs under conditions where parachutes would not provide sufficient accuracy. Later, work was undertaken to adapt the Rotochute so that it would provide initial deceleration for a manned capsule being returned from orbit. Working on the same principle as a helicopter, the Rotochute would be used to further slow the capsule's re-entry and guide it to a chosen landing site. Additional study

was then undertaken to test the feasibility of using Roto-
chutes in the return of large rocket boosters, nose cones,
and manned space capsules.

The company's first expense in 1945 had been for a pine
plank from which Mr. Kaman carved a rotor blade. It was
his urge to invent, improve, or make something better that
led him to develop a new kind of helicopter rotor blade.

"The early helicopter rotor blades were wood, then the
cry was for metal," he recently told a group of Wall Street
financial analysts. "We made wood blades and they worked
fine: then we made metal blades and they worked well too
but glass fiber blades are better than either wood or metal.
We have participated in the development of bonded glass
fiber as a material that will outperform anything else we
have seen. We have made glass fiber blades, tested them
thoroughly and flown them." Characteristically, glass fiber
blades were another first for the Kaman engineering team.

By 1963 the company's helicopter production was centered on the HH-43B Huskie, manufactured for the Air
Force, and the Navy-sponsored UH-2A Seasprite helicopter.
The Seasprite provided the Navy for the first time a helicopter that could meet its requirements for day or night
operation in all kinds of weather. As for the Huskie, since
1958 it had broken numerous world records, four of them
previously Soviet-held.

Although the company's two principal products were the
Huskie and Seasprite, Mr. Kaman did not feel it was wise
to concentrate entirely on this work. Furthermore, his urge
to carry on creative engineering led to diversification in lines
allied to his basic helicopter business. As a result, in addition to the helicopter manufacturing facilities, the Kaman
Aircraft Corporation diversification includes:

Kaman Nuclear in Colorado Springs, Colorado, to undertake nuclear research work for the government as well as to manufacture the Pulsatron, a commercial machine that generates neutrons which were formerly obtainable only from an atomic pile.

Kaman Instruments Division at Austin, Texas, to supplement and extend the work of Kaman Nuclear.

AirKaman at Bradley Field, Connecticut, to provide charter, sales and service for business aircraft as well as fuel and repair services for the commercial airlines operating at Bradley Field.

Special Products Division at Bloomfield, to concentrate on doing subcontracting work for others, fabricating, among other things, rotor blades, controllable-pitch ship propellers, and automobile springs from glass fiber.

Power Transmission Systems, Inc., at North Caldwell, New Jersey, to manufacture aircraft transmissions and do precision machining for the aircraft industry.

A sign on the driveway leading to the Kaman plant in Bloomfield reads: BEWARE. DURING SECURED HOURS THIS PLANT PATROLLED BY DOGS TRAINED TO PROTECT COMPANY PROPERTY.

This reflects another of Mr. Kaman's activities, the result of his friends' recommendation that he find himself a hobby to keep him from working so hard at the office.

"What should it be?" Mr. Kaman asked himself one day as he leaned on a fence rail, thoughtfully rubbing his long face and looking out over his 70 acres of pasture. He had enough to do now. Three children who live on a farm naturally involve their father as they raise plants, discover a rabbit's nest, help with the mowing and care for the grounds. There was his post as vestryman at St. Alban's Episcopal Church, the trusteeships he held in his alma mater and other colleges, the directorships in many voluntary organizations, the work with various civic groups, and the memberships in innumerable leading professional societies. Wasn't he busy enough already?

One day as he was patting the family's pet German shepherd dog he had the answer.

"Wouldn't it be fun to train German shepherd dogs?" he asked the children. "We can breed them for the blind, the police, and for many other jobs."

Cathleen, Charlie and Steven were delighted at the idea and Mrs. Kaman hoped the project would provide her husband with the relaxation he seemed to need.

Thus the Fidelco Breeders was born. Fidelco is a coined word from *fidelity* and *cooperation,* standing for the objectives of the little group composed of the Kamans and a few close friends. Kennels were built on the Kaman's property a distance from the house and within a short time the kennel had almost 20 dogs. Soon at the Kaman Aircraft Corporation's Bloomfield plant dogs were accompanying the guards who patrolled the grounds at night. Today, thanks to Mr. Kaman, the Hartford Police Department has one of the finest canine corps in the United States and Fidelco dogs are serving humanity in many ways throughout the country.

Another of Mr. Kaman's unusual hobbies evolved from his love for music. In 1952 he took up the bass viol, drums and other instruments and started to make recordings of them. To do this he built a home recording studio which is said to be surpassed by few commercial studios in the United States.

He teamed up with Ranger Andy, a popular television entertainer whose real name was Orville Andrews. Mr. Kaman and Mr. Andrews had to find time in their busy schedules when they could work together. It took six months of evenings and Sunday afternoon sessions to complete the "Songs of Ranger Andy," a high-fidelity long-playing record. The unusual musical accompaniments were created by Mr. Kaman. He played each of the instruments and by means of multiple recordings mixed and blended their sounds into harmonious background music that sounds as though many instruments were being played at once. A picture on the record sleeve shows Mr. Kaman plucking the bass viol, Ranger Andy singing, and the three small Kaman children sitting on the floor joining in the fun.

Recording was fun, but the growing demands on Charles Kaman's time forced him to give up this as well as other leisure-time activities. As the chief executive officer of a far-flung organization that was doing vital work for the Department of Defense as well as manufacturing numerous products and performing various service functions, he found that the 24-hour day was much too short for him. Who could have guessed when he hired Bill Murray to work with him in the converted cellar that less than two decades later his little company would be a major corporation worth $30,000,000 and owned by some 5,000 stockholders!

A sailor drifts helplessly in an open boat at sea and is rescued by a Seasprite helicopter. A valuable piece of electronic apparatus is retrieved from outer space by a Roto-chute. A scientist uses neutrons produced by a Pulsatron and makes an exciting discovery. A man reports for work and takes for granted the security of his job with its generous hospitalization, insurance, paid vacations, sick time and other fringe benefits.

. . . All these things could happen because a young man had an idea and was determined to make it work!

•

Chapter 10

MAN OF ACTION

THE manager of the big Chicago department store called the young man into his office.

"Frey," he said, "starting tomorrow you'll report for work at eight in the morning and work the regular evening shift too."

"But I can't!" the youth protested. "I'm finishing night school this year. I won't graduate if I miss classes."

"That's none of my concern," the man replied as he picked up a pile of papers. "If you don't want the job I know plenty who'll take your place."

Charlie Frey had no alternative but to work the 14-hour day, the only salary increase being a 35-cent allowance for dinner. It was 1904 and jobs were scarce. Working a 14-hour day was nothing new to Charlie and this setback only made him the more determined to get to college.

Charles N. Frey was born October 21, 1885, in Hopkins, a tiny town a few miles south of Grand Rapids, Michigan. His mother and father, Anna G. Klaus and August Frey, had six sons and two daughters, a large but extremely happy family. Charlie was perhaps closest to his older brother August who, like himself, had an inquiring mind that always had to know the *why* of everything. With young Charlie's help August built a telephone and together the boys experimented in their homemade laboratory with pulleys, light, sound and anything else that attracted their interest. Each day there seemed to be some new mechanical problem that needed solution.

Besides exploring scientific matters, Charlie was always asking himself the question: How did we get where we are? His quest for an answer took him again and again to his uncle's well-stocked library and later to the town library where he read books on his favorite subjects: history, philosophy, and economics. An avid and searching reader, he found the answers to many of his questions, but the more he read the more he wanted to increase his knowledge. Going to college became an absolute necessity to him.

Frey gained admission to Michigan State University, then Michigan Agricultural College at Lansing, Michigan, and he was able to make up the high school credits which he had lost when forced to work day and night at the department store. Thanks to his wide background acquired through reading, he passed all the college's economic and history requirements during his freshman year. This left him fairly free to pursue his favorite field—science, and more particularly chemistry—which, thanks to the guidance and encouragement of a friendly professor, soon narrowed into nutrition.

Wherever he looked there was something new to be explored, something unknown to be discovered. Most of all he wanted to get at the fundamentals of his favorite science and do experimental work.

There was little time for fun at college because Frey had to earn a good part of his expenses. During the school year he did various odd jobs and worked for the university's horticultural department, where he helped prepare and set out special plants for experimental purposes, made observations, kept records and tackled whatever chores were assigned to him. One summer he worked on a ranch in Wyoming. During other vacations he added to his classroom knowledge of agriculture and the growing of foods by hiring himself out to local farmers.

After graduation in 1911 he obtained a job teaching school in South Haven, Michigan, a small city on Lake Michigan not far from Hopkins, his home town. Never one to take it easy, he soon found a spare-time job working for the U. S. Department of Agriculture which was just starting its extension service in that part of the country. With Frey's extensive scientific training and his experience working on farms, he was well qualified to join the service that was designed to help farmers with their problems.

Up to that time there were few agricultural authorities to whom farmers could turn for assistance, and they lost no time bringing their questions to him. Some of the most pressing queries concerned blights and diseases which often plagued the extensive fruit orchards. It was up to Frey to examine the damaged fruit, identify the disease and advise a control. He analyzed various spraying materials and fertilizers to check purity and proper concentration. Matters involving soil conservation, soil fertility, better crop yields, and other typical farm problems challenged his scientific knowledge and ability to find solutions to the questions posed. He also introduced alfalfa, vetch and soya beans, and the limings of soils, and assisted the health officer in setting up a system of chlorinating the city water supply following a typhoid fever epidemic.

During summer vacations he took courses back at Michigan State University, working toward his master's degree, and during Thanksgiving, Christmas, winter and spring vacations, he attended meetings of the Academy of Science or visited agricultural experimental stations in different parts of the country.

In the fall of 1914 he entered the University of Wisconsin at Madison for full-time study and the following spring was awarded his Master of Science degree. That summer he worked for the U. S. Department of Agriculture on a unique national problem and helped to solve it.

Maine potatoes had been shipped to Florida to be planted and grown there, but soon the new crop was found to develop a disease, powdery scab, which covered the potatoes with a thick scab and made them inedible. Potatoes being such an important food, agricultural officials became alarmed and were most anxious to prevent the spread of the disease to other parts of the country. As a precautionary measure they placed a temporary quarantine on all shipments of potatoes from state to state until the cause of the disease could be ascertained.

Assigned to join a small group of agricultural experts, Frey traveled with them to Florida, then back up through the Southern states to Virginia, New Jersey and New York, collecting samples of soil and potatoes as they went. Outside Florida they found no potatoes with the scab, and even the experts were baffled.

Dr. Beatty, head of the Federal Horticultural Board, decided on a wider survey after Frey had advised that the Wisconsin and Minnesota potato-growing areas were somewhat similar to those of Maine but that the area had some high-temperature days, especially in southern Wisconsin and in the Red River Valley of Minnesota. Young Frey then obtained permission to go out to Wisconsin and Minnesota and look for signs of trouble in those states.

The professors at the University of Minnesota were not interested in cooperating.

"There's no powdery scab around here," they said emphatically and dismissed Frey's ideas as stupid. Undismayed and determined to track down the cause of the blight, he traveled up to northern Minnesota and the Red River Valley thinking that the people living there, some of whom had emigrated from Canada and New England, might have brought their own potatoes with them and introduced the disease. He went from farm to farm inspecting the soil and the potatoes, but nowhere within the southern territory or the Red River Valley did he find a trace of the scab disease.

At a Republican rally being held in Bemedji, a small town in the northern part of Minnesota, Frey happened to meet the governor, who took an immediate interest in the project. The next morning he sent for Frey.

"Yesterday you told me that you were looking for potatoes in Minnesota that have the powdery scab. Well, we don't have any here but I want to prove it. You and I are going to take my official car and visit some of the farms about here."

After numerous stops the young agricultural agent returned to the governor's car carrying several scabby potatoes.

"You have no disease in Minnesota?" he asked. "Well, look at these!"

Amazed, the governor stared at the potatoes and slowly shook his head in disbelief.

"We'll have to send them to Washington for positive identification by the lab," Frey said. "Until they are looked over we can't make a definite statement."

Thus ended the great potato mystery. The agricultural officials, including Frey, concluded that the disease was found in the colder regions of the north and in Florida only when potatoes were planted during the cool winter months. The disease would not normally occur in the areas between far north and far south when planting was done in warmer temperatures and where growth took place during warm weather. When this was verified, the quarantine was called off, farmers were advised not to plant any diseased potatoes and to select seed from areas where the scab did not develop or was properly controlled.

Returning to the University of Wisconsin in 1915, Frey became an instructor in the plant chemistry department in order to earn a living while working for his Ph.D. Before he had an opportunity to write the thesis required for a doctorate, the United States had entered World War I and the instructor-student was anxious to join his friends who were signing up for military service. When he talked of enlisting in the army certain military officials learned of his plans and summoned him to Washington. A few days later he was commissioned a first lieutenant in the Army's Sanitation Corps.

The Army was anxious to make a study of the food and nutrition needs of its men, and Lieutenant Frey was among the first ten scientists selected to undertake this program. In the course of his work he advanced to the rank of captain and visited innumerable camps, hospitals, and other army installations where he conferred with local authorities, studied the commissary plans of each, and noted the nutritional levels that were maintained.

While visiting the camp at Battle Creek, Michigan, he worked briefly with Julia Leary, a pretty medical technologist. Miss Leary had been a student at Wisconsin during Frey's undergraduate days and was now carrying on pathological work at the base hospital. This chance encounter sparked a romance that led to their marriage two years later. While Frey was at Battle Creek the great flu epidemic was raging, and he organized hospital facilities and developed special diets for the sick.

Reluctantly, Frey was about to return to Washington hoping for another assignment that would take him back to Battle Creek when he received orders to prepare for duty overseas, having previously requested foreign service. He and his group were to set sail immediately for Murmansk, Russia, up on the Arctic Circle!

At that time officers had to buy their own equipment. After spending over $600 for warm clothing, bedding, and other supplies needed for arctic living, Captain Frey heard the day before they were to sail that the Armistice had been declared and the trip canceled. He looked at the gear he had just bought and shook his head sadly. Then he smiled. What did it matter? The war was over and he could go back to Madison, write the thesis for his Ph.D., and later find time to visit Julia too. Instead he was assigned to Camp Meade, Maryland, where replacement troops were trained and it was a year before he could return to the University of Wisconsin.

In 1920, Dr. Frey received his Ph.D. after submitting his thesis which covered some of the studies made on the mechanism of disease resisters in plants and the nature of toxic substances secreted by fungi. Representatives of the Mellon Institute of Pittsburgh offered a fellowship that would enable him to undertake full-time research on yeast, one of his main interests. He plunged into this new work with enthusiasm, worked long hours, and at length evolved a process for making an active dry yeast which he immediately patented. Useful as his discovery was, the active dry yeast did not interest commercial producers because it was feared that it might cut into the sales of existing yeast. Up to that time all yeast sold commercially was fresh and had to be kept refrigerated, and it retained its fermenting power for a limited time only. Furthermore, there were manufacturing problems to be surmounted and much to be learned about dehydrating yeast in large quantities. Ten years later dry yeast was to become an important product for South America where poor transportation facilities made refrigeration impossible. It was not until about 1937, however, that yeast manufacturers in the United States again became seriously interested in active dry yeast.

The fellowship at Mellon Institute was discontinued at the end of 1921. Next Dr. Frey joined the Ward Baking Company as a research chemist. After part of that organization was acquired by the Fleischmann Yeast Company in 1924 he became a research chemist at the new Fleischman Laboratory in New York until 1926 when he was appointed director of the Fleischmann Laboratories, a post he held for the next nineteen years.

Three years later the Fleischmann Company, which dated from 1868, was merged with Chase and Sanborn, the Royal Baking Powder Company, and E. W. Gillette & Company, to make a new corporation called Standard Brands, Inc. This enlarged Dr. Frey's duties, for the other companies brought additional personnel, products, and problems into his research organization.

Dr. Frey saw his job as one that should provide leadership, coordination, inspiration, and a definite goal or objective to his research staff. At the outbreak of World War II his group numbered as high as 150 highly trained men, including the personnel in the central research lab as well as the other laboratories located in the many company divisions. For every chemist there is usually one technician, and besides these men and women there are laboratory assistants, clerical and secretarial workers. In a sense such a research department is the heart of a company which processes and manufactures food because the research staff is responsible for developing new products, improving existing ones, and acting continually as a watchdog to see that in compliance with Food and Drug regulations the highest degree of quality and purity is always maintained in the food that is produced.

Dr. Frey's wartime experience made him extremely conscious of the nutritional value of foods. He believed not only that foods should taste good and be attractive to the eye, but also that it is most important that they provide the nutrients which the body requires for growth, reproduction, energy and repair. He believed that by restoring the nutrients lost in the processing of basic foods, such as bread, cereal breakfast foods and margarine, the health and well-being of the population would be improved.

Under Dr. Frey's direction many notable discoveries were made in the laboratories. One of the most interesting involved a method of preventing rickets in children.

Dr. Steenbock of the University of Wisconsin had discovered that certain foods, when irradiated, would protect animals from rickets. At the Fleischmann Laboratories it was found that vitamin D was produced when yeast was irradiated with ultraviolet light. The high potency attained by irradiation made yeast and the irradiated sterol extracted from yeast excellent sources of vitamin D.

The first commercial production of vitamin D milk was carried out by the Fleischmann Laboratories and Walker Gordon Laboratories, then part of the Borden Company. The milk was prepared by feeding cows irradiated yeast which contained a high percentage of vitamin D. The

Fleischmann Laboratories prepared the standardized irradiated yeast to feed the cows and then tested it for its vitamin D potency by elaborate animal feeding tests. Each batch of yeast was carefully standardized to the same level and each day's production of milk was tested for its vitamin D potency at the Fleischmann Laboratories. Thus the levels of feeding necessary to produce a given potency in the milk were determined.

The amount of vitamin D required in milk to prevent rickets was found by feeding nearly 2,000 New York children who had rickets, and an equivalent number of controls was observed to check the experimental groups. The children were fed different levels of vitamin D milk prepared by the Walker Gordon Laboratories, and preventive and curative levels were determined after three years of work. The protective level found adequate in these experiments was accepted by the Food and Drug Administration as well as medical authorities and has not been changed to this day.

Another important project carried out under Dr. Frey's direction aimed at the enrichment of bread. During the depression of the 1930's when over 12 million unemployed were living on low incomes, bread was an essential part of the nation's diet. White bread was a low-priced food, it was tasty and an excellent source of energy. However, it had certain deficiencies in vitamins, minerals and proteins when compared with whole wheat bread. In general the public preferred white bread to whole wheat in spite of the fact that the latter was far more nutritious.

The Fleischmann Laboratories became interested in the problem of enriching white bread. Unfortunately the milling process which produces white flour greatly reduces the amount of thiamine, niacin, vitamin B_6, iron and riboflavin normally found in whole wheat flour. The task that confronted the laboratories was the replacement of at least thiamine, riboflavin and iron, and improving the quality of the protein and increasing the level of riboflavin to approximately that of whole wheat flour.

Many years of hard work both inside the laboratory and outside in cooperation with other companies and scientists finally produced a high-vitamin yeast that gave the public the necessary enrichment in its white bread. Today many states have adopted laws making enrichment of bread mandatory and about 80 percent of all white bread made in the United States is now enriched.

From 1945 to 1951, Dr. Frey served as Director of Scientific Relations for Standard Brands, using his administrative skills and know-how to coordinate the numerous facets of the company's research program. In this capacity he acted as the corporation's liaison officer with government agencies, professional societies, other concerns and research organizations.

Retirement from Standard Brands in 1951 after publishing some 120 scientific papers and obtaining over 60 patents did not mean that Dr. Frey's professional career was ended. The contrary was true, for now he had time to do many of the things his regular job had prevented.

There was his regular lecturing schedule at Columbia University's School of Public Health and Administrative Medicine and courses to be taught at Massachusetts Institute of Technology. There were consulting jobs to be done and innumerable meetings, conferences and other activities in connection with the many professional societies to which he belonged.

For instance, he has served as president of the Institute of Food Technologists, as well as a member of numerous advisory boards. There were dinners for Dr. and Mrs. Frey to attend where he was showered with honors—a D.Sc. from Michigan State University in 1946, the Stephen M. Babcock Award in 1953, the Nicholas Appert Award in 1954, the Honor Scroll of the New York Chapter of the American Institute of Chemists in 1956, Distinguished Alumni Award of Michigan State University in 1960, life membership in the Wisconsin Academy of Science, Arts and Letters in 1962, to name but a few.

There are visits to see the grandchildren, trips both here and abroad with his wife, and stacks of scientific journals, volumes of history, economics and philosophy still to be read. When I met Dr. Frey he was about to leave for a trip to Europe. He was planning to attend two international scientific meetings in London and then go on to Paris for discussions with scientists at the Pasteur Institute and to Rome for meetings with scientists of the Food and Agriculture Organization of the United Nations.

Few of us realize how indebted we are to men of action like Dr. Frey who, though retired from business, continue to work and share their scientific knowledge and experience with others for the betterment of all mankind.

Chapter 11

•

THE LURE OF BASIC RESEARCH

THE tall boy entered the principal's office at Ramsey High School.

"Did you send for me, sir?" he asked.

"Come in, Larry. I want to discuss your program for next year. You'll be a senior and I see you've been taking our classical course. You've had math, any reason why you haven't had a science?"

"No, sir." His face formed a shy but winning smile. "I never thought about it. Guess I haven't been particularly interested in that field."

"How about taking one course—say, chemistry—just to get a little balance? You should have some science, I think."

"Yes, sir," the student agreed, and the following spring Larry Darken graduated at sixteen with only one science course to his credit.

It is of course impossible to know what would have happened if the principal had not suggested the chemistry course. Unlike most of the men in this book who showed an early interest in science, Larry Darken could well have become a philosopher, a writer, or distinguished himself in one of a hundred ways, instead of becoming a scientist who has made notable contributions to the steelmaking industry.

Lawrence S. Darken was born in Brooklyn, New York, on September 18, 1909, the son of William Henry and Gertrude Stamper Darken. Little happened during his early years to indicate that someday Larry would become a famous scientist. He went to public school where he placed in the advanced section. Each day after the dismissal bell had rung he rushed outdoors to play. His father, also a native New Yorker, was in the insurance business and while Larry was still in grade school moved the family to Allendale, then a small town in a rural section of northern New Jersey. Later, at nearby Ramsey High, Larry went out for track and specialized in the high jump.

Just as it was the principal who had guided him toward science, so it was his mathematics teacher who was responsible for his choosing Hamilton. This instructor had just graduated from Hamilton and his enthusiasm convinced Larry that he should go there too. At college he plunged into the scientific field, making up for lost time. He majored in chemistry and mathematics but also took enough physics and philosophy so that either could have counted as a major.

To help supplement the scholarship which he had received, Larry spent five summers working at the huge A & P warehouse in Paterson, New Jersey, near his home. Here he did a variety of office jobs, starting as mail boy and working up to the statistical department, the supply room and the shipping department.

"Whenever someone went on vacation and they needed a man to fill his place, I was given the job," he recalled. "Actually it proved to be my only real business experience."

Although Larry studied hard at college he found time for track and fencing as well as making many friends. One who avoided recognition and preferred to stay on the sidelines, he was nevertheless popular, and it was no surprise to his friends when he was elected to Phi Kappa and named class valedictorian.

"Mother wanted me to become a doctor or a lawyer, but I took things pretty much as they came in those days," he said. "I really gave no thought to what I would do after college until the Christmas before graduation when my chemistry professor urged me to go on to graduate school."

The suggestion appealed to Larry, but he explained that he had no money to continue his education.

"That should be no problem," the professor assured him. "Get yourself a teaching assistantship in mathematics or chemistry. Write around to several universities and you're sure to find one."

Larry did as suggested and uncovered some prospects, but his need for financial assistance was unexpectedly solved when he was awarded a Root Fellowship which enabled him to enter Yale and work for his doctorate in the field of physical chemistry. During his first year he earned extra money serving as a laboratory assistant for the freshman chemistry course, and the following year for physical chemistry. During his third year he received a Loomis Fellowship.

"When I received my doctorate in 1933 the country was in the middle of the depression," Dr. Darken explained. "There was little prospect of a job for one who had taken his doctorate on ionization constants of weak acids in aqueous solutions. For that reason I accepted a fellowship that permitted me to continue for another year the work I had been doing."

How fortunate that was his decision! The following fall one of the new first-year graduate students working in the same field as Dr. Darken was an attractive young lady. Margaret FitzGerald had graduated from Hunter College in 1933 and had come to Yale to earn her doctorate. Since the chemistry building was located away from the main campus and the few graduate students spent most of their time working in the laboratory and in informal discussions, it was not long before Miss FitzGerald and Dr. Darken became good friends.

The following June Miss FitzGerald was as determined as ever to remain at Yale and earn her Ph.D. and Dr. Darken realized that if he ever hoped to support a wife he would have to find a job. Reluctantly he packed up his things, said good-bye to Miss FitzGerald and Yale, and returned to his family's home, then in Ridgewood, New Jersey. Once there he lost no time buying a commutation ticket on the Erie Railroad and went to New York City to seek a job.

"There's an opening in our research department for a chemist," an official of H. Kohnstamm Co. said. "It pays thirty-five dollars a week and you can start anytime." The company manufactured food colors and flavors and supplies for commercial laundries including soaps, acids, bleach and other products required in their operation.

"I'll take it!" Dr. Darken said, grateful for the job and eager to start work.

At that time the first formulas for making synthetic detergents were just being developed and Dr. Darken was told to invent a detergent that the firm could manufacture. He had no idea where to start or in what direction to go and the more he worked on the project the more discouraged he became. Actually it was to be a decade before detergents were developed to the point that Dr. Darken apparently was expected to achieve within six months' time.

A luncheon meeting rescued him from this unhappy situation. Dr. John Johnston, then director of United States

Steel's research laboratory at Kearny, New Jersey, decided that it would be wise to introduce more physical chemistry into the metallurgical research programs. He outlined his plans over the lunch table to Professor Blair Saxton, under whom Dr. Darken had worked for his doctorate.

"I know just the man " Professor Saxton exclaimed enthusiastically. "Larry Darken would be perfect for that job." Then he told Dr. Johnston why.

For Dr. Darken the opportunity to apply his training and knowledge in physical chemistry to a new field in which little research had been done in this country was irresistible. He gladly resigned his research job in the laundry field for what was to become a long and distinguished career in the steelmaking industry.

Fundamental research began in the United States Steel Corporation in 1927 when Dr. John Johnston, head of the Chemistry Department at Yale, accepted the newly created position of Director of Research. Overhead was kept to a minimum by using for laboratory quarters vacant space in the office building of the Federal Shipbuilding and Drydock Company (a subsidiary of U. S. Steel) at Kearny, New Jersey.

United States Steel Corporation is more than half a million people—employees and owners—who have pooled their skills and their capital into an industrial organization which has long been the nation's leading steel producer.

In size of total assets, U. S. Steel is the third-ranking American industrial company. Over a recent five-year period the company accounted for slightly more than 28 percent of the nation's steel production. Operations are conducted in its own name and through many divisions and subsidiary companies. United States Steel began business in 1901 with the chief purpose of producing steel more efficiently and economically. This was achieved by integrating its operations which included the entire sequence of steps in a manufacturing process from gathering raw materials to the production of finished products ready for shipment to customers.

When Dr. Darken reported for work at the Kearny laboratory it was difficult for him to visualize the size and extent of the company which he was to serve. Fortunately, from time to time, he was to have opportunity to travel and see some of the far-flung operations at first hand.

These included the vast fields of iron ore in Minnesota, Michigan, Alabama, Utah and even down in Venezuela; the coal mines deep underground in Pennsylvania, West Virginia, Kentucky, Alabama and Utah; the white Michigan limestone mines; and the deposits of manganese in Brazil and Africa.

Scores of cargo vessels plied the Great Lakes to transport ore and coal, and a half dozen railroad companies linked mines and ports with mills.

On Lake Michigan there was the tremendous plant at Gary, Indiana, with its fiery blast furnaces, its huge rolling mills, its hundreds of miles of railroad tracks. This, he found, was but one of more than a dozen steel plants that produced such items as coke, coal chemicals, iron, steel ingots, stainless-steel bars, rails, wheels, axles, steel and brass foundry products.

There was the tube division that manufactured steel tubular products; the steel and wire division that produced wire and wire products such as rope, fence, springs and nails; the bridge division that fabricated and erected bridges, buildings and many other steel structures; the cement division; the steel homes divisions; the oil well supply division; the steel products division.

Iron was initially made in the Saugus furnace near Boston in 1644 and the first steelworks were established in Trenton, New Jersey, in 1734. Since then most major advancements in steelmaking have resulted from research. Thus Dr. Darken found, when he first joined United States Steel, that he would be fairly free to explore and conduct research in areas of his own choosing, the purpose of the laboratory being to help United States Steel produce a better product for less money.

In the gigantic furnaces where iron and steel are made, at temperatures that may reach as high as 3,000° Fahrenheit, there were scores of processes which might be improved through research. A scientist like Dr. Darken would wonder about many things—whether the right proportions of the raw materials are being used, whether the temperature at which each batch is "cooked" is the optimum one, what alloys should be added to the mixture to increase the strength of the steel, how best the molten steel should be poured from the furnace when ready.

During the next two decades after Dr. Darken joined United States Steel, although he spent most of his time in the Kearny laboratory far from the nearest steel plant, Dr. Darken played as vital a role in the steelmaking operation as the foreman in charge of an open-hearth furnace. Day after day he conducted research quietly and methodically in many areas of physical and chemical metallurgy as he concentrated on thermodynamics and diffusion. His first assignment was to investigate the distribution of sulphur between slag and molten steel in open-hearth furnaces in order to facilitate the control of this element, which is usually considered harmful to the properties of the finished steel. After he had worked on this for more than a year, he presented his report to Dr. Johnston with the remark that implied, "Well, that's over." The wise director smiled and gently informed him that research problems seem to have a habit of not staying solved, and surely enough, Dr. Darken again came in contact with many ramifications of the sulphur problem later in his career.

He proceeded from this to the physical chemistry and thermodynamics of other elements in the high temperature range characteristic of iron- and steelmaking. One of his major investigations was with Dr. R. W. Gurry on the establishment of the phase relations and thermodynamics of the iron-oxygen system. This was undertaken because he considered it somewhat surprising that basic information on this system which lies at the very heart of iron- and steel-making was still somewhat fragmentary and not thoroughly established.

At about this time, while his primary interests centered on equilibrium relations at high temperatures, he was asked to review a paper on diffusion for one of the scientific journals. This was the first time that he was called upon to focus his serious attention on the matter of rates of reactions in solid metals. In looking into the available litera-ture in this area, he found serious gaps in the basic inter-pretation of some of these diffusion phenomena; thus he started in a new field of research in which he subsequently made many contributions, including the development of a set of relations which bear his name.

More recently the development of many new instru-ments and techniques has led to the development of a field known as metal physics. Among these instruments is the electron microscope which permits direct observation at very high magnification of phenomena which could never before be directly observed—but which were partly inferred from theoretical considerations. Dr. Darken kept in close touch with these developments and has made contributions in this field by adapting physicochemical techniques. In particular, he has investigated the interaction of the atoms of various alloying elements with the imperfections revealed by the electron microscope. He has investigated the factors controlling the rate of growth of pearlite, thus shedding light on some of the phenomena responsible for the hardening and strengthening of steel. He has also made contributions in areas not directly related to the steel industry.

One of the reasons Dr. Darken's experimental research experience was so unique was the fact that his pioneering efforts in science were achieved in a field where, until recently, few worked. This is not easy, because for the most part such a scientist must labor alone without the opportunity of being able to discuss his research, interchange ideas or benefit from the opinions and experience of others working in the same field.

"Those scientists working on applied research problems are usually assigned specific projects," Dr. Darken explained. "Often these jobs reflect sudden crises which must be solved immediately or they involve questions that require solution within six months to a year. In fundamental research, on the other hand, a good man dreams up ten times as many problems as he can tackle. Here long-range projects are studied that may take as much as ten years to solve. Therefore, a primary requisite for doing basic research is that a man must have his whole heart in his work and possess unlimited patience.

"Unlike the businessman who looks for part of his reward in terms of a better title and more status, the scientist who works for a corporation is interested primarily in seeing his professional abilities benefit the company. He rarely is elevated to a position that gives him status in business, but he is satisfied to receive his recognition from professional societies. Obviously he expects adequate pay for services rendered, but most scientists are happier working in their laboratories than in executive offices."

In 1939 Dr. Darken married Miss FitzGerald who, after receiving her Ph.D. from Yale, taught at Miseracordia College and then worked for Calco Chemical Company. The young couple settled in Westfield, New Jersey, and eleven years later moved to a much larger house in Short Hills. When not helping Mrs. Darken with the numerous problems and chores that arise in a growing family which eventually included six children, Dr. Darken also found time to author innumerable scientific articles as well as a standard senior and graduate textbook, *Physical Chemistry of Metals*, which he co-authored with Dr. R. W. Gurry. Thanks to his grounding in the liberal arts, Dr. Darken's papers were unusually well written and readable. Because of the reputation he had gained through his writing, Dr. Darken was asked to serve as adjunct professor at the Polytechnic Institute of Brooklyn where for several years he taught graduate courses on the physical chemistry of metals, metallurgical thermodynamics and phase rule.

The United States Steel management decided in 1954 to consolidate its research activities in the new Research Center at Monroeville, Pennsylvania. That same year Dr. Darken was appointed assistant director of the laboratory, and two years later when the Kearny laboratory personnel were transferred to Pittsburgh he moved his wife, six children, their pets and possessions out to a three-acre homesite on top of one of the foothills of the Alleghenies several miles from his new office.

The Research Center is situated on a partly wooded 144-

acre hilltop tract about fifteen miles east of Pittsburgh. The Applied Research Laboratories are housed in four buildings integrated into one unit, and the fundamental research laboratory, named the Edgar C. Bain Laboratory for Fundamental Research (for Dr. Bain, retired head of Research and Technology), is housed in a separate building nearby. The exteriors of the steel-frame, brick two-story buildings make effective architectural use of stainless steel.

Dr. Darken tells us in his own words about the Fundamental Research Laboratory:

"The responsibility of the Fundamental Research Laboratory is to further knowledge and understanding in those scientific and technical fields of current or potential interest to United States Steel. Our work, therefore, is largely in the basic sciences, and our technical personnel are primarily physicists, chemists and physical metallurgists. At present there are approximately 130 members on the staff. About one half of them are professional people, that is people with degrees in science or engineering, and of these professionals approximately half hold a Ph.D. or D.Sc. degree. For administrative purposes the Laboratory is organized into four divisions: Physics, Physical Chemistry, Physical Metallurgy and Chemical Metallurgy. We have, of course, our own necessary supporting services—library, design, drafting and photographic groups as well as machine shops—and these are supplemented when necessary by activities of the Applied Research Laboratory.

"While our primary responsibility is that of furthering knowledge, our staff is expected to be aware of the practical applications of its findings. The staff is urged to do enough applied research to demonstrate practical possibility. However, it is not compelled to do so. Laboratory management, of course, has responsibility to make sure that any potentially useful ideas are further developed either within the Laboratory, the Applied Research Laboratory or elsewhere. We also have a third responsibility and that is to act as consultants or to carry out special experiments for any activity within United States Steel when we are uniquely qualified to do so.

"Our scientific program is concentrated in three areas: strength and ductility, corrosion and oxidation resistance, and reactions that occur in transforming ore to steel. Our largest effort is in that of strength and ductility. Steels have risen to their prominence because of their outstanding combination of strength and ductility but there is an ever-present and ever-increasing demand for materials of greater strength-to-weight ratio, of greater ductility, of better resistance to deformation at high temperatures, of greater toughness at low temperatures."

In 1961 Dr. Darken became director of the Fundamental Research Laboratory.

Between telephone calls, discussing problems with members of the staff, attending joint meetings with scientists in the applied section, reviewing progress reports submitted by his personnel, attending to the administrative problems that invariably come up, and spending many hours with the numerous visitors who come to the building, he has found little or no time for research since his appointment.

Dr. Darken believes in giving members of his staff a minimum of supervision.

"Generally our scientists get satisfaction from seeing something of commercial and practical value coming directly or indirectly from their work," he said.

If a man needs aid he knows that Dr. Darken is ready

and eager to help, and in those rare cases where Dr. Darken feels that a man is falling behind in his work he tries to give him encouragement and assistance.

"In basic research it takes time to complete a particular research assignment," he explained. "Sometimes it happens that a scientist does not see any direct application to what he has done or discovered. In our industry changes are not made quickly because plants and equipment are too expensive to scrap overnight. Those who stay with us and stick to the job are usually extremely happy in their work and feel that in the long run—maybe years hence—they are contributing to the future of United States Steel."

To young men and women who are thinking ahead to a career in science Dr. Darken says: "Your big opportunity tomorrow will come if you are willing to cross fields to bring a knowledge, skill or technique that is already established in one area over into another area of scientific interest."

The public rarely learns about scientists like Dr. Darken because they spend much of their time working alone and what they accomplish is seldom headline news. It is, therefore, gratifying to know that such a man has received top recognition from the scientific world—election to the National Academy of Science—Dr. Darken being the third scientist associated with United States Steel to receive this high honor.

Fascination with science seems to run through much of the Darken family. Joanne, the firstborn, after graduating from the University of California, became a teacher of high school mathematics. Mary chose chemistry as her major at Trinity College, while Lawrence, the oldest boy, indicated interest in physics. Time will tell whether or not the other three children inherited their parents' scientific talents.

All is not science at the Darken home, however. After Dr. Darken has supervised the mowing of their acre of lawn, everyone gathers for family games of badminton and croquet. From time to time there is bowling, golf, tennis, and at one time the children enjoyed watching their father dismantle automobile motors—until he found that they had become too complicated. Evenings, when Dr. Darken is not catching up on his scientific reading, he turns to mystery novels and philosophy for relaxation, or if friends drop in, enjoys a game of bridge at which he is expert.

Dr. Darken's career is proof that basic or fundamental research which looks more to the future than the present can be as rewarding as other types of investigation. Progress will always depend upon scientists eager to tackle long-range projects who know full well that only future generations will enjoy the fruit of their labors and discoveries. In the long run perhaps this is the most important type of research.

•

Chapter 12

A NEW KIND OF PHOTOGRAPHY

A T the age of fourteen Edwin Land became interested in the problem of making a polarized filter for automobile headlights so as to eliminate annoying glare and reduce the danger of night driving. The idea so intrigued the young man that even after entering Harvard College he felt compelled to work on his polarizer again. He took a leave of absence, rented a room on Fifty-fifth Street near Broadway in New York City and set up a little laboratory. Determined to find the answer to what so far had been considered an insoluable scientific problem, he spent eight to ten hours a day reading and studying in the New York Public Library, after which he worked late into the night trying to perfect a thin sheet of material that would polarize light.

Ordinary light consists of a mixture of wavelike motions that move in all directions at right angles to the direction of its travel. Plane polarized light, however, is light whose vibrations lie in only one plane perpendicular to the path the light is traveling. By using a polarizer, or "director," it is possible to control light.

As a young boy Edwin had been interested in light rays and their behavior. Long before entering Harvard, he had

set up a research laboratory in his home where he conducted various experiments aimed at polarizing light. Born
in Bridgeport, Connecticut, on May 7, 1909, Edwin was
the son of Harry M. and Martha F. Land. After he had
attended the local Bridgeport grade school his parents sent
him to Norwich Academy where he prepared for Harvard.

By 1928 young Land had completed his first invention
and with the help of Julius Silver and Donald Brown, two
friends who were attorneys, applied for his initial patent on
a light polarizer for automobile headlights.

Land knew that the problem of controlling light rays had
intrigued scientists for more than a century. In 1818 the
French physicist Etienne Louis Malus peered at the win-
dows of the Luxembourg Palace through a piece of calcite
(calcium carbonate, with hexagonal crystallization) and
found that it extinguished the glaring image of the sun.
Other crystals acted in the same manner, but large pieces
were so rare and expensive that they could be used only
in laboratories. In 1852 Dr. William Bird Herapath discovered that when iodine was combined with quinine salt,
tiny crystals were formed that were capable of polarizing
light rays. Further observation revealed that some layers
of crystals were transparent while others were opaque and
transmitted no light. Soon Herapath realized that all of the
crystals were transparent and became opaque only when
one was placed crosswise over another. Unfortunately he
was never able to make a satisfactory crystal that would
serve as a useful and inexpensive artificial polarizer, nor
did anyone else until Edwin Land tackled the problem and
found the solution.

Making smaller crystals—thousands of them—not larger
ones, as Herapath had attempted, was the clue to the
mystery. Eventually Land worked out a method for incor-

porating the microscopic rodlike iodo-quinine crystals in a thin sheet of transparent plastic. When the plastic was stretched, the needlelike crystals aligned themselves parallel to each other, whereupon the plastic was "frozen" and placed between layers of thin cellophanelike material, glass or other transparent substances. The sheet could then be cut in any desired size or shape.

A source of light does not send out vibrations in an orderly pattern, but in a helter-skelter fashion very much like a bottle brush whose bristles stand out at right angles to the wire core. When the light vibrations strike the polarizer, all are stopped except those which arrive lined up with the invisible optical grain of the crystals. The principle is the same as if you picked up some bamboo sticks and threw them at a picket fence. Only those sticks would go through that were thrown parallel to the open slats. Although many scientists recognized the value of polarizing light, few had considered how it might have any practical application to everyday living. It was therefore surprising to Mr. Land, when he filed his first patent for a polarizer to be used on automobile headlights, to discover that five other patent applications had been filed with the idea of polarizing headlights.

In 1929 Land returned to Harvard to continue his undergraduate studies and also to work on his elementary polarizer. Although he had filed a patent application on his crystal-suspension light polarizer, he wanted to improve on his original process.

One secret of Land's later success was his constant insistence on improving what he had done. He was never satisfied that an invention was perfect. The university officials were impressed with what their returning student had accomplished and assigned him the use of a laboratory so that he might continue his research and experiments. Here he met George W. Wheelwright III, a physics instructor, who became interested in Land's polarizer. The two men became close friends.

It was in 1932 at a Harvard symposium that Land first publicly disclosed his polarizer. It comprised a sheet of cellulosic material which incorporated millions of oriented submicroscopic, needle-shaped crystals of herapathite. His process might be considered the very opposite of his predecessors' attempts to grow large crystals. The sheet was made by first forming a doughy mass of crystals which were scattered and embedded in a plasticized carrier. This mass was then forced from a press under such conditions that the needle-shaped crystals embedded in it all lay in the same direction. The resulting product was a sheet approximately three feet wide and of any desired length. There was no competitive material on the market—in fact, no polarizer of any kind was available at anything like the price for which this material could be sold profitably.

Edwin Land had too much on his mind to continue his studies as a Harvard undergraduate. Although he needed to complete only a few additional courses to earn his B.A., he never did. (In spite of this Harvard awarded him an honorary D.Sc. in 1957.) Both he and George Wheelwright were so anxious to get busy with new experiments that it took little persuasion to get Wheelwright to resign his teaching position and go into business with him. In a cellar on Boston's Dartmouth Street they established the Land-Wheelwright Laboratories, offering the public a general consulting service in physics. The country was in the depths of the depression and at first the partners were not overworked with assignments. When the patent on Land's polarizer was finally granted in 1934, the two men began to spend all of their time working on various commercial applications of Land's brainchild. Land worked out an arrangement whereby he licensed Eastman Kodak to manufacture photographic light filters called Pola-screens, the agreement providing that Land would furnish the polarizing materials for the filters. Thereafter, the Eastman revenue helped to finance the operation of the laboratory.

The following year Land suggested to the American Optical Company the possibility of using the polarizer for sunglasses, and they sent a representative to see what the product would do. Realizing that the humble cellar laboratory would not provide a suitable meeting place, Land rented a room on the sunny side of the nearby Copley-Plaza Hotel, and prior to the arrival of his visitors carefully placed a tank of goldfish on the windowsill where it would catch the sun's rays and produce a dazzling reflection.

When the company official arrived, Land pointed to the tank that reflected the sun's glare and asked the man if he saw any fish.

"Of course not," was the reply.

"Then look again through this," Land said, and gave the official a sheet of what appeared to be darkened cellophane.

"Amazing!" the visitor exclaimed. As if by magic the glare was gone and he could clearly see the fish swimming about in the water. This was indeed a remarkable invention, one that the official readily saw would bring profits to his company. He was familiar with all kinds of sunglasses and knew that the most expensive merely darkened the view but did not cut down the objectionable glare. As in the case of the camera filters, the sunglasses would black out the reflected polarized light which is responsible for most of the glare, and would only allow useful light rays to come through the lens. Within a short time "Polaroid" sunglasses were coming off the production line and proved an immediate hit with the public.

In 1936 Land agreed to a public demonstration before a group of industrialists and scientists to show them what other possibilities there were for using polarized light. Among the amazing applications he showed were a system for eliminating automobile headlight glare, a 3-dimensional movie in full color, a variable density window for controlling the brightness of a view, plus a number of other less impressive applications.

One thing was becoming clear to Land and his associates: if they were going to develop some of these promising polarizers they would need more money. Although there was a steady income from Eastman Kodak and American Optical Company, there were by no means enough funds to finance a better and larger laboratory and pay the salaries of the enlarged research staff which Land wanted to hire. Through a friend, the twenty-eight-year old inventor was introduced to Schroder Rockefeller Company and Kuhn Loeb & Company who arranged the initial private financing by such influential financiers in New York as James P. Warburg, W. Averill Harriman, Lewis Strauss and others. They were impressed with the young man and his inventions and when Land established the Polaroid Corporation in 1937, they provided the company with $375,000 in capital under an arrangement which left Land in control of the company.

Few brand-new corporations have started with a board of directors made up of such distinguished men. There were Harriman, Warburg, Strauss, Land's old friends Donald L. Brown, patent attorney, and Julius Silver of the law firm of Silver, Saperstein & Barnett, and banker Carlton Fuller, who later left the presidency of Schroder Rockefeller Company to join Polaroid as treasurer.

From 1937 to 1941 sales zoomed from $142,000 to $1,000,000 a year. The sunglasses continued to sell, the filters were a popular Kodak item, and a new Polaroid study lamp that was glare-free was placed on the market and sold well. For the New York World's Fair that opened in 1939, the Chrysler exhibit demonstrated Land's 3-dimensional movies for which the viewer had to wear special Polaroid glasses.

The deception was so perfect that many viewers tried to approach or touch the automobile projected on the screen. The principle responsible for these movies was similar to that found in the old-fashioned stereoscope. The stereoscope is an instrument that lends a 3-dimensional effect to photographs. By looking through two lenses at two slightly different views of the same scene placed side by side, a 3-dimensional illusion is created.

A double camera was used to take the moving pictures for the Polaroid demonstration. The lenses were about three inches apart, and two separate films were exposed, one for each eye. When projected one over the other on the same screen, one lens was polarized horizontally for the right eye, the other vertically for the left. The viewer wore specially polarized glasses so that each saw only the proper picture, the brain supplying the 3-dimensional impression. The results were highly satisfactory, but from a commercial point of view a simpler system was indicated.

In 1938 Joseph Mahler, a Czechoslovakian experimenter, came to America to work with Land. Together they created an entirely new method of producing 3-dimensional movies by placing the two individual images together on the same film. Thus the film would be shown through one standard projector and special Polaroid glasses worn by the audience would separate the pictures so that each eye would see only the image taken for it.

Mahler joined the firm, and working closely together, Land and he devised a new process which they called the "vectograph." Before it became possible to develop it further for commercial use, war made it necessary to adapt the vectograph to various military uses. Thanks to this invention it was now possible to make training films which would give the viewer the illusion of three dimensions, and aid in teaching many subjects. Vectograph slides enabled navigation students to study the heavens indoors and view the stars in their true 3-dimensional relationship. One unusual application was to provide naval ships with vectographs taken of military objectives. This enabled the gunners to gauge heights, depths, and distances with greater accuracy as they trained their weapons on the enemy. Complicated machinery could be projected on a classroom screen and every part clearly seen. Later, vectographs were adapted for patients who needed to exercise certain eye muscles to improve their eye convergence. Salesmen found that vectograph slides enabled them to give a customer the illusion of inspecting a huge piece of equipment right in his office.

Adapting the vectograph for military use was but one of the many ways that Land and the Polaroid Corporation aided the war effort. Land headed several research teams which were entrusted with responsibility for developing plastic optical elements, infrared night vision instruments, lightweight stereoscopic range finders, infrared searchlight filters, infinity optical range sights for antiaircraft guns and other weapons.

At the same time the company undertook the manufacture of filters for military goggles, periscopes, range finders, gun sights, aerial cameras, and the Norden bombsight. Wearing variable density goggles, Air Force gunners were able to look close to the sun while aiming at enemy aircraft. Other types of filters were used to eliminate glare for men on submarine patrol, to help adapt the eyes of bomber crews to the dark, and to add a 3-dimensional effect to reconnaissance photographs.

In addition to supervising the manufacture of the above items, Land directed the development of a guided missile, and served as a consultant on guided missiles for Division Five of the National Defense Research Council. No wonder honors and awards poured in on both Land and Polaroid for their participation in the war effort!

In 1945, the last year of heavy war contracts, Polaroid's sales reached almost $17,000,000, but with the return of peace, government contracts were canceled and the following year sales dropped to $5,000,000. Land needed something big to help him get back into peacetime production and keep the expanded organization busy. He knew what it should be, for there still remained his lifetime dream that he hoped would someday be a reality—glareless headlights. Actually, it was the promise of this invention that had sparked so much interest among the financiers who had helped raise the original $375,000 in 1937 (and another $375,000 in 1939). Land had not only been able to obtain a patent on his polarizer but he was also able to purchase the patent rights on the headlight scheme from the man who had been deemed the original inventor.

Before the United States entered World War II there had not been enough time to perfect the device and persuade the automobile manufacturers to place Polaroid filters on all new cars. Land tested his invention repeatedly and found it worked perfectly.

"What farsighted physicists have long appreciated," Land wrote, "was that if the headlight lenses and windshields could be made of optical 'picket fences' with the pickets parallel to each other, and at, for example, forty-five degrees to the road, the headlight problem would be solved. For it is apparent that each driver would see his own light as it illuminated the road, because the rays reflected by objects illuminated by his headlights would pass through his windshield; whereas his windshield would have its optical slots crossed with those of an approaching headlight."

In 1947 Land conducted tests at the General Motors proving ground and his system passed all of the visibility requirements laid down by the engineers. It looked as though his years of work would at last meet with success and a profitable future be assured for the company. Then came the news—Detroit said *no*. The automobile manufacturers saw no easy way of equipping the 33,000,000 automobiles then on the road with the same system and they feared that drivers of these cars might find it hard to adjust to the brighter headlights on filter-equipped vehicles.

Dr. Land was amazed. Polaroid headlamps made such good sense. Everyone agreed that they would cut night accidents and make driving after dark much safer. He could not believe that this was a final turndown but felt certain that someday this sensible and much-needed improvement would come. He was positive that it would be the Polaroid Corporation that would supply the filters.

Dr. Land was disappointed but not discouraged, even though that year his company showed an operating loss of $2,000,000 with sales of only $1,500,000. Fortunately the young president had so many interests and ideas for new products that he always had something to which he could turn. Right now he had an invention which would be even greater than glareless headlights.

The idea was sparked during the war on one of those rare times which Dr. Land was home with his family. It was a bright sunny day and he was taking pictures of his daughter.

"How soon can I see the pictures, Daddy?" she asked impatiently.

Dr. Land explained why it took so much time to get the films developed, printed, and back to the customer. Then suddenly he realized that this was all wrong. A person should not have to wait days or weeks before he could see his pictures. Why couldn't a camera be manufactured that would develop and print each picture immediately after it was snapped?

As if he were not busy enough with his wartime duties, Land somehow found time now and then to work on his newest problem. How could he create a process that could work in a camera small enough to be carried conveniently and replace all those processes performed in a laboratory darkroom which develop and print pictures? Most people would have declared the idea impossible.

The obstacles to producing a camera that could develop and print a picture within 60 seconds seemed almost insurmountable. Film, process and camera—all had to be invented and made to work. Nothing like this combination camera-developer-printer had ever been undertaken before.

At a meeting of the Optical Society of America held February 21, 1947, Land demonstrated his new one-step photographic process. The program hailed it as "a new kind of photography as revolutionary as the transition from wet plates to daylight loading film." Land clicked the shutter, turned a knob on the camera, waited a minute, and pulled out the finished picture!

Next came the problem of marketing a camera that sold for $80 to $90 in competition with models that cost only a few dollars. With no sales force and a tiny advertising budget it was decided that the best way to introduce the novel camera would be to give photographic dealers and one department store in each city an opportunity to be the exclusive dealers for a month—provided the stores would advertise the camera extensively.

In Boston the camera went on sale November 26, 1948, at Jordan Marsh. Dr. Land and everyone in the organization held their breath and waited to see what would happen. Would people, in general, and in great numbers, be willing to spend almost $100 for a camera? Many experts, namely the amateur photographers, the financiers, the camera dealers, said *no*: the camera would be just a novelty. Furthermore, would the public buy a brand-new product with the maker's word their only guarantee that it would work?

All doubts and fears proved groundless, for the Polaroid Land camera became an immediate hit. Crowds swarmed into the large Boston store to buy this amazing new invention and salesmen had to be restrained from selling display models that lacked vital inside parts.

During 1949 Polaroid's sales leaped to $6,680,000. To this record the new Land camera and special film had contributed $5,000,000. Since that time the company has introduced many improved models, color film, and has also featured an "electric eye" shutter which automatically provides correct exposures for all outdoor lighting conditions. Polaroid's total sales in 1962 came to more than $103,-000,000 and Polaroid Land cameras have been outselling all other cameras in their price range put together. Patent protection should keep the cameras from serious competition until at least 1970.

It is interesting to note that with the manufacture of the first cameras Dr. Land adopted a policy of making nothing that could be purchased from an outside manufacturer at an acceptable price. Accordingly, most Polaroid Land cameras have been manufactured by the U. S. Time Corporation and other contract manufacturers. This policy frees the staff at Polaroid to concentrate on research, development and manufacture of film and other products that call for Polaroid's special skills.

Dr. Land rarely gives an order. Instead, he guides the affairs of the company by discussing problems with his associates, encouraging and helping them to see things clearly and then delegating full responsibility for the job to be done. Convinced that every human being has the ability to create if he is given the chance, Dr. Land tries to inspire those about him to achieve success on their own, and nothing pleases him more than sharing the joy of discovery.

Two of his close associates are Meroe Morse, now manager of black-and-white film research, and Howard Rogers, manager of color film research. Miss Morse, an arts major at Smith College, joined the firm during the war, and found the challenge of a scientific research laboratory more stimulating and rewarding than a career in art. She has been responsible for many important developments, especially in film research. Howard Rogers followed in the footsteps of his boss, leaving Harvard after one year to join the Land-Wheelwright Laboratories. He too has made many extraordinary contributions to the company's research program.

Dr. Land's greatest concern is that all employees have jobs which in some way or other they have created for themselves, built around their own interests, personalities and skills, so that the working experience may be a happy one. If Dr. Land has his way Polaroid will someday be famous for being the first company in the world to recognize the dignity of every employee and give him full scope for his abilities each day that he reports to work. His new factories are being designed so that the machines work for the employees instead of the employees for the machines.

This is Dr. Edwin H. Land—a gifted inventor to whom over 250 patents have been issued solely and jointly; a famous scientist, honored with memberships in many distinguished scientific societies; a part-time educator who serves as a visiting institute professor at M.I.T.'s School for Advanced Study; an astute businessman who built an organization from a crude cellar laboratory to a hundred-million-dollar business housed in more than a dozen modern buildings; but more than all of these, an industrialist who believes in the dignity of the individual and who does something about that belief.

Chapter 13

•

THE SYSTEMS CONCEPT

"**N**OW we add sight to sound," declared the Radio Corporation of America's David Sarnoff on April 30, 1939, at the dedication of the New York World's Fair.

Television, he said, "is a creative force we must learn to utilize for the benefit of all mankind."

Not only was this program the first public introduction of television in the United States but more important, it subsequently added another major industry to our economy, a business that depended upon our best engineering brains for its birth and continued growth. By the early 1960's, some two decades after television's unusual debut, RCA had spent over $180 million in scientific research and commercial development of black-and-white and color television, and new vistas of growth still lay ahead.

It was a day of great personal triumph not only for David Sarnoff, but also for a young scientist who had played a key role in translating Sarnoff's concept of commercial television into technical reality. Many brilliant men had contributed to this successful event but it was Elmer Engstrom who, in his quiet thoughtful way, had brought a new philosophy to RCA's television development program—"the systems concept"—which perhaps more than any other single engineering contribution was responsible for the rapid progress made in perfecting this miraculous invention.

Elmer William Engstrom was born in Minneapolis on August 25, 1901, the son of Emil Engstrom, a power plant engineer, and Anna Nilssen. The family moved to St. Paul shortly after Elmer was born. There he attended elementary and high school, then studied electrical engineering at the University of Minnesota where he received his B.S. in 1923. The soft-spoken young engineer stood five-feet, seven inches tall, later acquiring the nickname of "Shorty." He had a quick smile and intelligent quizzical eyes.

Immediately after graduating he went to Schenectady, New York, to join General Electric. Three years earlier, the first major radio broadcast had reported the returns of the Harding-Cox Presidential election. By the time Mr. Engstrom reported for work the radio business was booming and he was assigned the job of conducting research on transmitters to improve their strength, quality and range. In 1926 he switched from transmitters to receivers, since the best transmitter was valueless unless there was a good receiver to pick up and amplify its signals. This job did not last for long, however, because the bright young scientist was needed to head up a newly formed group which was to undertake engineering on sound motion picture equipment, from which work the RCA Photophone System was soon developed.

In 1930 certain radio engineering and manufacturing plants of General Electric were transferred to RCA. This corporation had been formed in 1919 at the request of the government to provide an international communications service for our nation. When organized, RCA stock was issued to General Electric and Westinghouse, among others, and later to the American Telephone & Telegraph Co. (To this day RCA is still active in the business for which it was organized, operating a world-wide communications network through RCA Communications, Inc.)

During the 1920's RCA not only conducted its globe-encircling radio communications service but also became involved in radio broadcasting, principally as the owner of the pioneer radio network, the National Broadcasting Company. It also acted as a research and engineering operation, and sold home radio receivers manufactured by General Electric and Westinghouse.

For better understanding of RCA and Dr. Engstrom's subsequent connection with it, we must go back to April 14, 1912. That night twenty-one-year-old Russian-born David Sarnoff, a radio operator for the Marconi Wireless Telegraph Company of America, was on duty at his wireless set.

Suddenly he received the news of the *Titanic's* distress signal and of what had happened. He promptly made that news available to an anxious world. From the rescue ship *Carpathia,* Sarnoff received the list of survivors and other important messages related to the disaster. He stayed on duty continuously for 72 hours, during which time President William Howard Taft ordered every other wireless station along the East Coast silenced to prevent interference. Sarnoff's efforts during the *Titanic's* rescue operations won him national fame.

Three years later Sarnoff was urging his employers to manufacture a "radio music box," and he envisoned the day when every home in America would be equipped with one. Then, when he became commercial manager of the newly formed RCA, his idea was adopted. Between the years 1922 and 1924, sales of radios totaled $83,500,000.

In 1929, RCA purchased the old Victor Talking Machine Company of Camden, New Jersey. This gave RCA not only the famous Victor name but more important, its first manufacturing facilities. Shortly thereafter, RCA acquired other manufacturing facilities from General Electric and Westinghouse, and entered into the manufacture and marketing of its own radios. Finally, in 1932, the government ordered General Electric and Westinghouse to sell their stock interest and withdraw their representatives from RCA's Board of Directors. Since that time RCA has been entirely on its own.

The top engineers of radio's early days came to Camden, New Jersey, where the RCA research laboratory was located. Men like Vladimir K. Zworykin, famous for his invention of the iconoscope, were among them. Young Mr. Engstrom, who had been shifted from General Electric at Schenectady to RCA's Camden plant, was surrounded by men of outstanding talent.

Commenting on an article and picture of Engstrom that appeared in the February 1934 issue of *Broadcast News,* a later editor said, "No one who knew that curious menage would have prophesied that the quiet young man with the cherubic countenance would someday rule the lion cage —and that he would go on from there to run the greatest electronics company on earth."

For this young man was not only a scientist—he was also an astute organizer and administrator. The exigencies of television's development soon brought this to light. Elmer Engstrom's first research group was relatively small, but there was much to do and the engineers had to work quickly. It was 1931 and RCA was about to make the first field test of a complete television system. Elmer Engstrom—having already served apprenticeships in transmitters, receivers, and in sound motion pictures—was ready. The brand-new Empire State Building was invaded (the first of many times) and a transmitter installed high on the 85th floor. A mechanical scanner provided a 120-line 24-frame picture from both live and film subjects. Extensive field tests were made using the first cathode ray tube receivers. Although the pictures left much to be desired, the equipment worked well as a system and the tests proved that a successful television broadcasting service was possible.

In this new organization which was embarking upon unknown electronic ventures, the young scientist received from David Sarnoff—often called the "Father of American Television"—an opportunity to demonstrate his talents as an organizer and administrator. In addition, he brought a unique philosophy to the television development program.

"None of the engineering groups working earlier on television had gone deeply into the basic systems problems involved," Engstrom later recalled. "We set out to get a better understanding of what it took to achieve television standards of high enough quality for regular broadcast service to the public. This made it possible for us to set our sights at just the right level to best accommodate the requirements that would be made as television became a service to the public. We knew that we had to put a system together, test it as a system, then go back over the components to improve the system and test it again."

This was a pioneering application of the "systems concept" that now figures prominently in all large-scale electronics programs. As an advocate and director of the development effort, Engstrom was instrumental in the achievement of the practical commercial television system that was introduced by RCA at the New York World's Fair in 1939.

For the next twenty years this scientist was to be in the

very center of RCA's television development, and taking an ever-increasingly important part in it. His research responsibilities were gradually broadened to include apparatus, systems and tubes for all RCA activities. By the time television was introduced by David Sarnoff at the World's Fair, the name of Elmer Engstrom had won widespread recognition throughout the industry as an outstanding research director.

In 1942 when the research activities of RCA were brought together at Princeton, New Jersey, in the newly organized RCA Laboratories, Mr. Engstrom was appointed director of general research. The modern three-story building was a far cry from the little tent erected in Riverhead, Long Island, in 1919, to serve as RCA's first laboratory. World War II was raging on several fronts and Elmer Engstrom knew that he must immediately organize the diverse talents of all the members of the staff. It was not easy, but he had worked with these engineers and scientists during the early television experiments. He knew what each could do and how to harness their various abilities to best advantage. Under his direction the research group compiled a brilliant wartime record in radar, shoran, sonar, airborne television, infared, radio thermics and many other facets of communications and electronics.

On December 7, 1945, four years after Pearl Harbor, Mr. Engstrom was elected vice-president in charge of research of the RCA Laboratories Division. There was much work to be done, for with the end of the war came the problem of reorienting to peacetime pursuits. Again television became the big thing in electronics. Black-and-white (monochrome) transmission had at last become a reality.

Considering the fact that the first television broadcast, as a regular service to the public, took place in 1939 and that during the war years most research was concentrated on military projects, there had been little opportunity for the television manufacturers to improve their black-and-white receivers. When RCA introduced the first postwar black-and-white television sets in September, 1946, a new industry was born. Today there are more than 60 million black-and-white receivers in use in this country.

Even while it was pioneering black-and-white television, RCA had already begun experimenting with color transmission. Actually, within six weeks of the 1946 introduction of black-and-white, RCA's engineers were able to demonstrate an all-electronic color television system.

During the interminable field tests, hearings and reviews which followed, Elmer Engstrom directed RCA's technical efforts in color. He also served as one of the vice-chairmen of the National Television Standards Committee (NTSC), the industry committee which studied and recommended the color standards eventually adopted by the FCC.

"We are convinced more than ever," Engstrom told a Congressional committee, "that the only system which would succeed is a compatible all-electronic system."

His abilities, already well recognized within the electronics industry, began to be noticed by others. In 1949, New York University conferred on him the honorary degree of Doctor of Science. The citation read in part:

> "Elmer W. Engstrom . . . one of that exclusive group of latter-day Private who not only illumines with his own brilliance, but who yokes his fellow Titans unrenowned for tractability into corporate resourcefulness and fecundity."

Convinced that an all-electronic, compatible color system would be superior to a mechanical system, Sarnoff and

Engstrom in the fall of 1949 spurred development at RCA Laboratories of the tricolor picture tube, the key to the all-electronic color system.

Night after night, the scientists and engineers worked late, testing; trying new ideas, testing; introducing new circuits, testing. Within months, the RCA 3-gun tube was perfected, in time to demonstrate to the FCC in March, 1950.

On October 10, 1950, the FCC dropped a bomb into the industry when it authorized an exclusive standard for a system of broadcasting color television which had been proposed by the Columbia Broadcasting System (CBS). This was a mechanical color wheel method, in contrast to RCA's electronic system. Although the FCC stressed the color fidelity in approving the CBS invention, most manufacturers criticized the system because it was not "compatible" with black-and-white TV—that is, a color picture could not be received in monochrome on a black-and-white set.

RCA's attorneys appealed the FCC ruling in the courts, and further development of the RCA system was carried on. The fight against the color wheel system continued, and in December, 1953, the FCC approved standards for a compatible system.

The following year, after spending tens of millions of dollars on research, RCA proudly introduced color onto the market. RCA was the first company to bring out color television, but sales were slow for several years. However, color then began to capture the interest of the set-buying public.

By the end of 1962, virtually the entire industry had entered the field of color television production. Had it not been for David Sarnoff's faith in color television and his vision in continuing the spending of money so that Dr. Engstrom's researchers could further improve their product, color television might have died. The battle had been won at last.

Occupied as he was with the problems of producing the compatible color system, Dr. Engstrom's responsibilities were greatly extended in 1954 to include all engineering throughout the corporation. His subsequent career reflects the growing importance of sound technical management in an era of technology. The next year he was appointed senior executive vice-president of the company, with RCA's defense activities and product planning added to his direction of research and engineering operations.

His record of achievement in steadily widening areas of responsibility finally elevated this quiet, scholarly-appearing man to the president's post on December 1, 1961.

Speaking of this scientist whose many assets include a remarkable ability to think and act simultaneously as a scientist and as a top-flight business executive, General Sarnoff said, "Dr. Engstrom's selection reflects our confidence in his ability and his experience, particularly in those areas where RCA anticipates great future growth."

If there were any who wondered about the ability of a technical man to cope with the commercial, financial, and marketing side of the business, Dr. Engstrom dispelled such doubts in short order. A few months after his election he took part in a meeting of the distributors who handle RCA consumer products across the nation, and he demonstrated such a detailed understanding of their problems that he received a standing ovation.

One bedazed merchandising expert collared an RCA executive at the end of the session and commented, "The guy knows more about the consumer business than we do!"

In its makeup today, RCA's technical organization bears the visible stamp of Dr. Engstrom's influence through years of research and engineering management. An example is the energetic program of basic research by RCA scientists. This stemmed from an Engstrom decision of the 1940's that industrial laboratories must contribute in the quest for new scientific knowledge.

A further example is RCA's thriving space electronics program, the responsibility of the Astro-Electronics Division, which was established at Dr. Engstrom's instigation in 1956 as the first major space research and development organization within the electronics industry.

Another illustration is RCA's success in the field of major electronics systems, typified by the immense BMEWS project (Ballistic Missile Early Warning System) and the versatile family of RCA electronic computing and data-processing systems. These resulted directly from the energetic application of the same "systems" philosophy that sparked the television effort of the 1930's.

Dr. Engstrom still retains the habit of working directly with the operating managers throughout the company, most of whom are his personal friends and associates of long standing. Within the corporate headquarters in the lofty RCA Building at 30 Rockefeller Plaza, New York, he handles his affairs informally, unlike most busy executives who are surrounded with push buttons and secretaries. He is as likely as not to leave his own office to drop in on a subordinate for an individual discussion or a group meeting. As a result, in the view of his staff, a pleasant personal touch is added to the transaction of business with a minimum loss of time to all concerned, including Dr. Engstrom himself.

Besides the 53rd-floor President's Suite in the RCA

Building, Dr. Engstrom makes use as often as possible of offices that have been maintained for him at the RCA Laboratories in Princeton and at the company's manufacturing and engineering complex at Camden, New Jersey. He frankly enjoys walking through the laboratories and engineering facilities to obtain a firsthand view of technical activities and to discuss their implications with the scientists and engineers on the job. In this way he keeps abreast of new technical trends and maintains personal relationships, many of which date back to his days as a young engineer.

Dr. Engstrom is married to the former Phoebe Leander, who is also a Minnesotan by birth. They have one son, William Leander. For many years, Dr. Engstrom has been an active community leader in Princeton, playing a leading part in the affairs of the Princeton Hospital, the YMCA-YWCA, the Princeton Chapter of the American Red Cross, and the Rotary Club.

A deeply religious man, he and Mrs. Engstrom are leaders in the Westerly Road Church of Princeton, and Dr. Engstrom manages to find time at the end of a busy day to speak to Bible study groups now and then. Steadfastness has been called his outstanding trait but he is also quiet in mien, courteous in speech and honest in everything he does. Although naturally reserved he remembers, and is quick to acknowledge, the thousands of acquaintances he has made over the years.

Today, he finds that the responsibilities of the RCA presidency leave him far less time than in the past for either community or personal activities. He regards as compensation, however, the fact that the added demands relate entirely to the electronics science and industry in which he has always found such a challenge and stimulation.

The continued business leadership of RCA, the advancement of electronics and the strength and security of our nation depend, in Dr. Engstrom's opinion, upon the encouragement of personal talents.

"In this respect, there is no great difference between research, management, government or the multitude of other organized human activities," he said. "Everywhere we must seek out and make the most effective use of our intellectual resources. There is need for creative imagination in all of our affairs—especially at a time when there is so much to be gained by . . . science and technology, and so much to be lost by their perversion to selfish or shortsighted ends."

In 1962 President John F. Kennedy alerted the nation to the great need for more engineers and scientists. He said:

". . . One of the most critical problems facing this nation is the inadequacy of the supply of scientific and technical manpower to satisfy the expanding requirements of this country's research and development efforts in the near future."

In spite of this need for trained scientific manpower in the United States, engineering enrollments in colleges decreased during the years 1958–1961, with less than 68,000 young people enrolling in the latter year. Only half of the would-be engineers receive a B.S. degree and educators report that there will be a continuous decline in the number of engineering graduates through at least 1965.

On the other hand, a survey made in 1961 of 517 companies and government agencies which employ 200,000 of the nation's 900,000 professional engineers showed that by 1971 these employers will need 45 percent more engineers than they had in 1961. It is clearly evident that those who remain in college to earn engineering degrees will be assured good jobs. A good engineer who has initiative, ability and a real desire to forge ahead should have no worry about his future. The men whose lives we have sketched in this book are proof of that.

Our nation's destiny lies partly in the hands of its future engineers and scientists. By the year 2000 there will be approximately 370,000,000 Americans whose needs must be provided. Energy sources must quadruple between 1963 and 2000. The atomic power industry will have to develop and possibilities in solar power and release of energy in controlled thermonuclear reactions must be explored. There will be great discoveries in geology, ore recovery, and metallurgy to provide for our wants in the face of diminishing supplies of important raw materials. Industry will research, manufacture and use new materials which are unknown today. By 2000 many of the products in use will be new to a person living in the 1960's.

Not only will the trained technical expert have to develop tomorrow's products and processes, but also many companies will expect him to provide the executive leadership needed to get the job done. Our nation will turn to the engineer and scientist as it prepares for these great new frontiers.

INDEX

187